NUMBER CORNER
TEACHERS GUIDE

BRIDGES IN MATHEMATICS

K

written by
Donna Burk
Allyn Snider

illustrated by
Tyson Smith

Published by
The MATH LEARNING CENTER
Salem, Oregon

BKNCTG-1

Number Corner Kindergarten Teachers Guide

The Number Corner Kindergarten Package consists of—

Number Corner Teachers Guide

Number Corner Blacklines

Number Corner Overheads

Poems & Songs Portfolio B

Number Corner Calendar Markers

Number Corner Components

Number Corner Manipulatives

The Math Learning Center, PO Box 12929, Salem, Oregon 97309. Tel. 1 800 575–8130.

© 2007 by The Math Learning Center

All rights reserved.

Prepared for publication on Macintosh Desktop Publishing system.

Printed in the United States of America.

QP130, QP84 and QP156 BKNCTG-1

P0807 **11166_SALBLU**

Number Corner is a year's worth of skill-building lessons and assessments. A key component of the *Bridges in Mathematics* K–5 curriculum, it can also be used to supplement other mathematics curricula.

The Math Learning Center is a nonprofit organization serving the education community. Our mission is to inspire and enable individuals to discover and develop their mathematical confidence and ability. We offer innovative and standards-based professional development, curriculum, materials, and resources to support learning and teaching. To find out more, visit us at www.mathlearningcenter.org.

This project was supported, in part, by the National Science Foundation. Opinions expressed are those of the authors and not necessarily those of the Foundation.

ISBN 9781886131767

acknowledgements

Book Design
Susan Schlichting

Cover Design
Susan Schlichting and Tyson Smith

Layout and Graphics
Christy Peterson, Vaunie Maier, Travis Waage,
and Susan Schlichting

Illustrator
Tyson Smith

Editorial Consultants
Dr. Albert B. Bennett Jr. and Dr. Gene Maier

Production Editor
Vaunie Maier

Materials Production
Tom Schussman and Don Rasmussen

Technical Support
Dan Raguse

. . . .

We give special thanks to
Kathy Pfaendler, Linda Foreman, and Gene Maier for being our teachers and mentors over the years. Their insights
and understandings have helped us grow.

Dr. Rosemary Wray for her priceless friendship and
continued support in the area of student assessment.

Dr. Amy Driscoll for teaching us the difference between
assessment and evaluation.

Beth Ardell, Becky Boergadine, Jill Board, Andy Clark, and
Cheryl Ogburn for their unflagging devotion to teachers
and children everywhere, the hours of thoughtful reflec-
tion and conversation they've shared with us, and their
willingness to try new things.

Dona Beattie and Bob Nicholas for basic support in the
form of food, keys, money, computers, parking permits,
and faith.

Mary Baratta Lorton, Kathy Richardson, and Marilyn Burns
for being original and continuing sources of inspiration.

The late Dr. Michael J. Arcidiacono for his vision, quiet
spirit, sense of balance, and extraordinary teaching skill.

Dr. Debra Kosaka and Melinda Garcia of Oak Grove School
District, San Jose, California, for their moral support.

The teachers who field-tested *Bridges in Mathematics*,
Kindergarten, allowed us to observe its implementation
in their classrooms, and/or permitted us to explore new
ideas with their students. In particular, we thank: Peggy
Steinbronn, Des Moines, Iowa; Sharon LeBlond, Bronson,
Florida; Nancy Goldsmith, Jen Eaton, Beck Sosa, San
Jose, California; and Kim Holsberry, Vacaville, California.

We also wish to acknowledge the many children who
have been involved with the field-testing of *Bridges in
Mathematics*, Kindergarten. As always, their enthusiasm,
intelligence, and candor has taught us much and been
quite influential in shaping the program.

And finally, we thank our families for their incredible
patience, support, and encouragement.

table of contents

February

Day 100

March

April

May & June

An Interactive Bulletin Board

The Number Corner lessons and routines revolve around the classroom calendar. New pieces added to the display each day become the basis for problem solving and skills instruction. The Number Corner should be set up on a bulletin board around which all students can comfortably gather. After an initial startup period of three or four days at the beginning of each month, Number Corner sessions average about 10 minutes a day, and should be used in conjunction with *Bridges* Problems *&* Investigations and Work Places or other ongoing math instruction.

There are four basic Number Corner components: a calendar grid to which daily markers are added, a chart that tracks the children's month in school, a birthdate chart, and a paper chain to which a link is added for every day the students come to school. There are also routines that are introduced at different points during the year in order to teach a particular skill or concept and then are phased out after a month or two. Altogether, there are eight Number Corner routines; a description for each follows. These routines provide a basis for ongoing instruction in sorting, patterning, graphing, probability, counting, numeral recognition, comparing, addition, shapes, money, and time. The Number Corner complements the instruction in Kindergarten *Bridges*, but will also work well with most other kindergarten math programs.

The Calendar Grid

The Calendar Grid opens in August or September with shape markers arranged in an ABCDABCD pattern. A new marker is posted each day, and after several days, children name the colors, describe the shapes, and begin to make predictions about what will come next. While not all children will grasp the first month's pattern in its entirety, every youngster will learn at some level, perhaps learning color names and one-by-one counting, along with some shape names and their attributes. Students' confidence grows as the pattern repeats again and again.

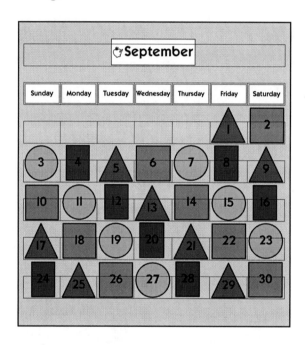

Starting in October, students make their own markers for the grid. This heightens their investment in the calendar, and gives them the opportunity to figure out how they want to pattern their markers. Student-made calendar markers also help to provide a wonderful sense of renewal each month. We have suggested ideas each month, some of which are designed to complement *Bridges* themes as they emerge through the year (bugs in the fall, quilts and sea creatures in the winter, and frogs and toads in the spring) Student-made markers can also be tailored to fit other classroom themes as well.

Our Month in School

A card is added to the Our Month in School pocket chart each day the children come to school. Although the cards themselves vary from month to month, their purpose is to mark the number of school days in one way or another.

In September students post one number card each day they come to school. Card 21 marks the 21st day they've been in school.

September

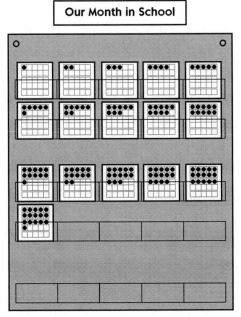

October & November

In October students remove the number cards from the chart and post weather cards instead. Later in the month, the data is transferred to a graph, where it is saved to compare with the weather data collected in November.

In December and January, the focus turns to counting and understanding numbers to 20 and beyond, with cards that show one new dot for each school day. The dots are organized on ten-frames. In December they help students learn to count by 5's and 10's, and in January they help children explore odd and even numbers.

December

January

In February, the cards for this special pocket chart deal with money (pennies and nickels). In March and April, probability and data collection are featured. In May and June, the cards provide children with opportunities to practice counting by 5's and 10's.

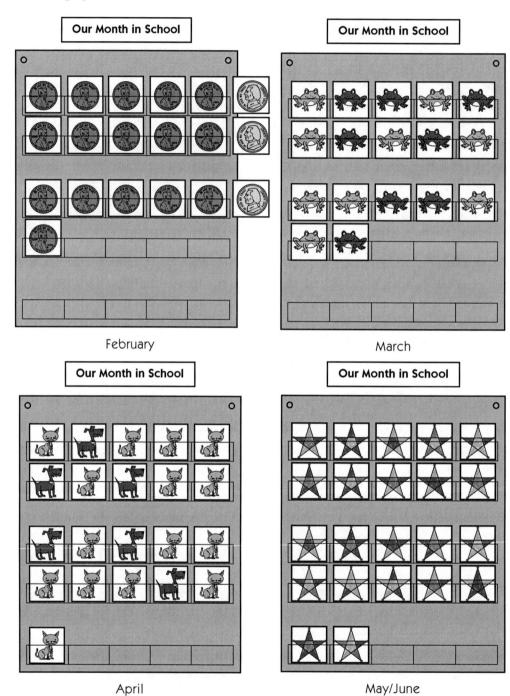

February

March

April

May/June

A Link Each School Day Building the Yearlong Paper Chain

On the first day of October, children work together to make a paper chain with as many links as days they have come to school. The chain is made with 10 loops in one color, 10 in a second, and any remaining days are shown in the first color again. The September chain is hung in a location separate from the calendar display.

We were in school 21 days in September, so we made 21 links—10 and 10 more and 1 more—21 in all.

In the calendar display, students begin a new chain each month, and add a link for each day they're in school, using the same two colors all year long. At the end of each month, this chain is added to the yearlong chain so students have a running total of how many days they've been in kindergarten. The links alternate in color every 10th day, thus serving as another tool to help children learn to count by 10's as well as 1's. In January, special number labels are attached to the growing chain to highlight the groups of 10 and to provide students with opportunities to learn to recognize the "counting-by-10's numbers."

After the 100th link has been added, which usually happens in early to mid-February, a second section of the yearlong chain is started. At the end of the year, both sections are joined and displayed in a prominent location in the room, or even out in the hall for everyone to see.

Here's When We Were Born

At the beginning of each school year, a birthdate marker is created for each child and hung below students' birth months. This chart is used to keep track of upcoming birthdates, and also to help children learn the names of the months in sequence.

Later in the year, the markers are posted on the calendar grid itself at the beginning of each month, so children can more easily count the number of days until the next birthdate.

The Kid Count

This routine, introduced in December and phased out at the end of January, gives children a compelling reason to count and read numbers to 20 and beyond—taking attendance. In the Kid Count, children learn to count off around the circle to find out how many students are in class on any given day. They also use a new counting chart to help determine how many children, if any, are absent.

1	2	3	4	5	6	7	8	9	10
11	12	13	14	15	16	17	18	19	(20)
21	22	23	24	(25)	26	27	28	29	30
31	32	33	34	35	36	37	38	39	40

🐱 The Kid Count chart 🐭

"We usually have 25 kids in class, but today there are only 20."

In a variation of the Kid Count also used during these two months, each child in class is given a number card. These are distributed in random order, and after giving students a minute to help each other determine how many dots they have on their cards, the teacher asks children to line themselves up in order. The number cards for this activity use the same ten-frame format as the cards on the Our Month in School chart, providing youngsters with yet another opportunity to encounter quantities that have been organized in groups of 5 and 10.

In January, the routine of clapping and counting around the circle to determine how many children are in class is enhanced with a song that sets the counting numbers from 1 to 20 to a pronounced beat. In this version of the activity, the children, each holding a Kid Count number card, line themselves up in order, sit down where they are, and then stand back up when their number is sung.

. . . .

Yesterday, Today & Tomorrow

This Number Corner component first appears in January, and is designed to help children begin to discuss and understand the language and concepts of past, present, and future. It revolves around a label with three headings—yesterday, today, and tomorrow. In January, a class art project or worksheet is taped under each heading, and then moved as the days pass and today becomes yesterday, while tomorrow becomes today.

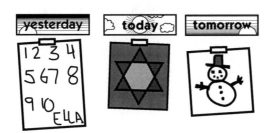

"Yesterday we practiced writing our numbers. Ella let me borrow her work to put up."
"Today we're going to make snowflake designs with pattern blocks to decorate the room."
"Tomorrow we're going to make snow people."

In February, the Yesterday, Today, Tomorrow card is used to record significant classroom events, which gives students a chance to reflect on past events and take a hand in planning future ones.

The Hundredth Day

The Hundredth Day activities are a special Number Corner feature to help you celebrate the hundredth day of school, whenever it may occur. If your school year begins in late August or early September, you'll probably hit the hundredth day sometime in February, so these four special activities can be found at the end of that chapter. The first activity in the collection involves a game of 20 questions in which children collect clues to identify a special treat you've hidden away—a bag of individually-wrapped candies. In the second activity, students estimate how many candies are in the bag, count them onto ten-frames to find out, and then work together to determine how many of the candies each child can have. In the third activity, each child makes a crown decorated with 100 stars. In the fourth and final activity, each king or queen strings an edible necklace—100 cereal O's grouped into sets of 10. All four activities are designed to give children a better sense of the number 100.

The Bean Clock

In March, you'll move into a more specific consideration of time by talking with your students about some of the things they do in the morning, the afternoon, and the evening, and recording their ideas on a three-part chart. This chart becomes part of the Number Corner display for the month, along with a clock with beans representing each minute. Teachers set the clock to a given hour each day and relate the time represented on the clock to an event meaningful to the children.

Blackline NC 29

Bean Clock

Teacher I've set the clock to 10 o'clock in the morning. That's when we have our recess.

This is only the first of a series of activities introduced during the spring months to help kindergartners begin to develop a sense of time, understand how people use a clock to measure it, and begin to learn to read a clock face to the hour.

Here's When We Were Born Graph

Introduced in May, the Here's When We Were Born graph is a more compact version of Here's When We Were Born, which will allow the class to honor everyone's birthdate, especially those children born in the summer, and will also provide some practice over the month at reading and interpreting information on a graph. Early in May, each child colors and labels his or her own marker. The markers are collected, sorted by month, and posted on the graph one month at a time, over a two-week period. Each time a new row of data is displayed, the children discuss the information, considering such questions as, "Which month has the most birthdates so far?" and "How many markers are on the graph so far? How did you count them?" and "Were there more birthdates in February or March? How many more?"

After all the markers have been posted on the graph, the summer birthdates are marked as a way of recognizing the children who won't be at school when their special days arrive.

Here's when we were born.

☃January	Ronnie Jan. 14	Maria Jan. 24				
February	Suzy Feb. 8	Dan Feb. 11	Matt Feb. 27			
March	Kari March 4	Ellie March 13	Marty March 26			
April	Ligia April 2	Julie April 17	Jorge April 18			
May	Debra May 1	Mike May 30				
June	Taylor June 6	Randy June 15				
July	Sammy July 4	Maxine July 17	Dianne July 25			
August				Our Special Summer Birthdates!		
September	Ronald Sept. 6	Javiar Sept. 20				
October	Tommy Oct. 3	Leslie Oct. 19	Hector Oct. 30			
November						
December	Nancy Dec. 16					

Questions From Teachers About the Number Corner

The Number Corner includes many different components. How can I possibly cover so much material in 10 minutes a day?

First of all, it's important to understand that there are no more than 6 components featured in any given month, and usually only 3 or 4 (see below). While some of them need to be updated each day, few require daily discussion. You may ask a student helper to update some of the components before Number Corner time, while reserving other components to do with the group. In January, for instance, you may use the Yesterday, Today & Tomorrow routine and the Kid Count some days, while emphasizing the Calendar Grid and the Our Month in School chart on others. Your focus will change from month to month, depending on the components featured, but also week to week and day to day, depending on your instructional needs.

Number Corner Components Featured Each Month	AUGUST / SEPTEMBER	OCTOBER	NOVEMBER	DECEMBER	JANUARY	FEBRUARY	MARCH	APRIL	MAY / JUNE
The Calendar Grid patterning, counting, numeral recognition & calendar reading skills	O	O	O	O	O	O	O	O	O
Our Month in School Chart counting, data collection, probability & money	O	O	O	O	O	O	O	O	O
Yearlong Paper Chain counting by 1's & 10's		O	O	O	O	O	O	O	O
Here's When We Were Born Chart months of the year, duration	O	O	O	O	O	O	O	O	O
Kid Count counting & reading numbers to 30				O	O				
Yesterday, Today, Tomorrow Card yesterday, today & tomorrow					O	O			
Bean Clock morning, afternoon, evening & time to the hour							O	O	O
Here's When We Were Born Graph reading & interpreting information on a graph									O
Day 100 Activities counting by 10's, estimation & number sense						O			

The other thing to remember is that it will take your entire math period during the first few days of each month to have children clear away the old Number Corner display, to make the new calendar markers (and, some months, to develop a pattern for the markers), to add the paper chain links from the previous month to the yearlong chain, and to become familiar with the new cards for the Our Month in School chart and any other new components you're introducing for the month. Once these things are done, the routines for the month should compress to an average of 10 minutes a day. Each chapter includes complete plans for the first three or four days of the month and then offers suggestions for designing daily 10-minute sessions around the new routines for the remainder of the month.

How can I keep students engaged day after day?

Even though the Number Corner routines change from month to month and sometimes even within the same month, it can be challenging to keep students consistently engaged and interested. From our own classroom experience, we can offer the following tips:

• Make sure that your Number Corner is posted in a good location. (See notes under the next heading for more advice about this.)

• Once they're up and running each month, keep your Number Corner sessions short and lively. We recommend that you aim for 10 minutes per session, even if children are very involved. It's better to leave them wanting a bit more than feeling as if things have gone on too long.

• Don't try to do every component each day. Choose two or three components to feature each session and have a student helper update the others before you start. Your selection may be based on trying to present an even balance over a week's time, or it may depend on your instructional targets at any given time, or the needs and interests of your group.

• Use the Number Corner as a teaching tool. While you may want to have student helpers update certain components of the Number Corner before some sessions, we strongly recommend that you lead the routines and lessons yourself. Very few kindergartners are skilled enough to facilitate the kind of problem solving and basic skills instruction needed to make the Number Corner work effectively.

• You probably won't get to the Number Corner every single day. Once you've established the new routines for the month and have returned to your regular math instruction, there may be a few days in a month when you skip it altogether. It can easily be caught up a day or two later.

Where do I set it up in my classroom?
It is essential that the Number Corner be set up on a wall adjoining a group meeting area where children can gather comfortably for as long as 30 minutes. (Even though most sessions shouldn't exceed 10 minutes, the amount of sitting time is longer during the first few days of each month.) This group meeting area needs to be large enough for children to sit facing the display wall.

The pinning surface for the Number Corner will need to be about 7 feet wide and 6 feet high. If you don't have any bulletin board area this big, consider fixing cork board or styrofoam to part of an existing chalkboard. If you really can't manage a pinning surface of any size, both of the Number Corner pocket charts have grommets, and can be suspended in some way from the top of a chalkboard or on a pocket chart stand, while the rest of the components can be attached to the board or a nearby wall with tape or other adhesives.

How much time does it take?

For the first three or four days of each month, the Daily Routines will take anywhere from 20 to 45 minutes each day. In these first few Getting Started lessons, children will create the new calendar markers for the month and become familiar with any changes or new components. After this initial period of three or four days, the Daily Routines will compress to an average of 10 minutes a day, and you'll be able to return to your regular math instruction, which may be whole- and small-group lessons and independent games and activities from the *Bridges* kindergarten program or one of the other math programs currently available for early primary children.

Why should I use the Number Corner as part of my math instruction?

If you are already devoting 30 minutes or more each day to math instruction, you might well ask why you should take another 10 minutes a day for Number Corner. There are several compelling reasons.

• *The Number Corner provides daily exposure throughout the entire year to a wide range of concepts, and practice with critical skills.*

Many kindergarten math programs feature units that focus fairly heavily in one particular area, such as patterning, sorting and graphing, counting and numeral writing, geometry, or early number operations. While this kind of curricular design makes it possible to study certain areas in depth over prolonged periods of time, or to complete projects that require specific kinds of mathematics, it can be challenging to also provide the kind of broad based exposure and practice children need on a daily basis.

Skills like counting; numeral recognition; understanding quantities to 10, 20, and then 30; copying, extending, translating, and creating patterns; sorting; graphing; comparing; recognizing coins and starting to count small sums of money; early time telling; and beginning computation require frequent practice throughout the year. Furthermore, children develop understandings at different times and at different rates. A child for whom extending an AABAAB pattern is an utter mystery in the fall may begin to make sense of the idea much later in the year, given consistent, but renewed exposure month after month. A unit on sorting and patterning provides an introduction to big ideas, but children need repeated opportunities throughout the entire year to copy, extend, translate, and create many different patterns. The Number Corner ensures that children receive constant practice throughout the year with all the skills considered to be building blocks of a good kindergarten program.

- *The Number Corner is rich in both problem solving and basic skills practice.*

The Number Corner has been written to correlate quite closely with the NCTM Standards (see below).

NCTM Standards Correlation Number Corner, Grade K	NUMBER & OPERATIONS	ALGEBRAIC THINKING	GEOMETRY	MEASUREMENT (TIME & MONEY)	DATA ANALYSIS & PROBABILITY	PROBLEM SOLVING	COMMUNICATION	REASONING & PROOF	CONNECTIONS	REPRESENTATION
August / September	O	O	O			O	O	O	O	
October	O	O			O	O	O	O	O	
November	O	O			O	O	O	O	O	
December	O	O	O			O	O	O	O	
January	O	O		O		O	O	O	O	
February	O	O		O		O	O	O	O	
March	O	O		O	O	O	O	O	O	
April	O	O		O	O	O	O	O	O	O
May / June	O	O		O		O	O	O	O	

As suggested by these Standards, the Number Corner routines provide problem-solving opportunities, even as they teach basic skills. While there are examples of this kind of instruction throughout the lessons, a particularly interesting instance is found in March and April during the Our Month in School routine. The children themselves make the cards for both months by coloring in simple frogs and toads, and later, cats and dogs, to create a set of 30 cards—15 of each creature. The routine itself is simple too—the arrow is spun on a spinner to decide whether a frog or toad (and later, a cat or dog) will be posted in the pocket chart each day.

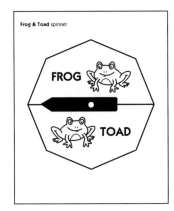

The problem posed to students is whether frogs or toads will come up more frequently over the month. The investigation begins anew in April with cat and dog cards and a different spinner.

The difference in the two spinners and data gathered over a month's time give children opportunities to develop and modify theories about which animals are most likely to win and why.

As mentioned above, the results are posted on the Our Month in School chart and graphed. They are also recorded in the form of number sentences, and in April, children are encouraged to develop their own forms of notation to represent the results.

- *The Number Corner illustrates the importance of math and its connection to everyday routines.*

Children who believe that the only real math is number based have an opportunity to discover that math also involves patterning, sorting, geometry, data collection, probability, and measuring. The Number Corner encourages young learners to explore concepts of time and duration—past, present, and future; yesterday, today, and tomorrow; morning, noon, and night; how long until and when will it be time?—in a meaningful context. Over the months, they have extended opportunities to understand how and why people use calendars, clocks, and money.

What materials will I need for the Number Corner?
Aside from a wall display area, teachers need the following materials:
- Number Corner Teachers Guide and blacklines
- Calendar Grid pocket chart
- Our Month in School pocket chart and cards
- day, month, and year labels for the Calendar Grid and the Birthdate chart
- other materials for daily routines (the Bean Clock, the number labels for the yearlong paper chain, the Kid Count chart and cards, the Yesterday, Today, Tomorrow card, the Number Corner captions, the monthly pattern strips, the Frog & Toad spinner, and the Cat & Dog spinner)
- the Songs & Poems Portfolio A

There are also two trade books featured in the lessons—*Benny's Pennies* by Pat Brisson and *Frog and Toad All Year* by Arnold Lobel, and a cassette tape and CD as well—*Songs for Number Corner by Greg and Steve.*

Teachers who wish to use the Number Corner with minimal financial outlay can purchase the Economy Package, which includes a Teachers Guide, blackline masters, and a Poems & Songs Portfolio, along with blackline masters to make the Number Corner components and materials for the daily routines. Books and tapes can be purchased from many educational supply houses or The Math Learning Center, and there are instructions below for making the Calendar Grid and the Our Month in School pocket chart.

The Deluxe version of the Number Corner includes the Teachers Guide and blacklines, along with all the instructional materials, display charts, the two books, and a cassette tape and CD. This option is more expensive, but much less demanding in terms of teachers' time and effort. All instructional materials are ready for classroom use. Students will still make calendar markers each month after August and September.

NUMBER CORNER	PACKAGE OPTIONS		
	DELUXE	ECON +	ECON
Print Materials			
Number Corner Teachers Guide & Blackline Masters	★	★	★
Poems & Songs Portfolio A	★	★	★
Markers & Components			
August/September Calendar Markers	★	★	★
Winter Break & Day 100 Calendar Markers	★	★	★
Number Corner Components	★	★	
Blacklines to make the Number Corner Components			★
Wall Charts			
Calendar Grid Pocket Chart	★		
Our Month in School Pocket Chart	★		
Books & Cassette Tape and CD			
Benny's Pennies	★		
Frog and Toad All Year	★		
Songs for Number Corner by Greg and Steve	★	★	★

The Economy Plus package falls between the Economy and the Deluxe versions in terms of what it requires from teachers. It includes the Teachers Guide and blacklines, along with the various instructional materials, but requires teachers to make or purchase the Calendar Grid and the Our Month in School pocket chart. It also assumes that teachers already have, or can buy, the books.

The Number Corner also requires some basic classroom supplies, including
- construction paper
- chart paper
- copier paper
- cardstock suitable for copying machines (about 100 sheets of white)
- butcher paper
- a class set of individual chalkboards or white boards, along with chalk or markers and erasers
- crayons
- glue

Number Corner basic classroom supplies
- scissors
- paper clips
- watercolors and tempera paints, along with brushes
- glitter (this is optional, and you only need a small amount)
- green, yellow, and brown Unifix cubes (about 50 of each)
- a classroom pocket chart

Making the Here's When We Were Born Chart & the Helper Jar

No matter which kit you buy, you'll need to make two things before the school year starts. One is a set of birthdate markers for the Here's When We Were Born chart. To do this, run several copies of Blackline NC 1 on cardstock or construction paper. Cut the cards apart and fill them in for each child in class.

If you teach double session, you might want to run the markers on two different colors before you fill them in so it's easy to tell the two classes apart once the cards have been posted.

The second thing you'll need to make is a set of popsicle sticks, laminated strips, or durable markers of some sort labeled with children's names for use in choosing helpers for various tasks during Number Corner lessons.

We place these in a plastic container—the "helper jar," we call it—and use them throughout the entire year, both during the Number Corner and in our *Bridges* lessons. Before we ever use the jar to select helpers, we take all the sticks out and read them to our students to assure them that their names have all been included.

Making a Calendar Grid

The Calendar Grid pocket chart comes with the Deluxe kit. If you'd rather buy the calendar grid than make it, it's available from The Math Learning Center, catalog number LCGPC.

You can also make this grid by overlapping two pieces of 24″ × 36″ oak tag, gluing, and then trimming to form a 29″ × 31$\frac{1}{2}$″ sheet, as shown. This sheet then needs to be marked off into six rows of 4$\frac{1}{2}$″ × 4$\frac{1}{2}$″ squares, and labeled with the days of the week along the top. (You'll find a blackline for these labels in the Economy materials blacklines. Run a copy, cut out the labels, and glue them into the appropriate boxes on your Calendar Grid.)

If you have a bulletin board for your Calendar Grid, hammer straight pins into the upper center of each daily box to hold the markers. If not, use a sharp point such as a school compass point or nail to poke a hole and run one prong of a brass fastener through from the back side of each box. Be sure it is pointing upward on the calendar side and then flatten and tape the remaining prong (and head of the fastener) on the back side. The markers (when they have been punched with a standard hole punch) will hang easily over the exposed prongs.

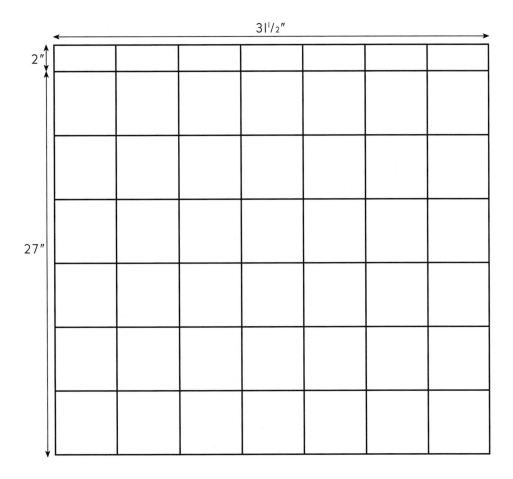

Making the Our Month in School Chart

This chart also comes with the Deluxe kit. If you'd rather buy the Our Month in School chart than make it, it's available from The Math Learning Center, catalog number OMSC.

You can make this pocket chart from poster board (any color—blue or yellow might be nice), cut to 24″ wide and 28″ long. If you have a rolling laminator at your school or district office, gather some of the discarded laminate pieces. Use them to cut strips 2″ × 20″ and tape them to the poster board as shown to form 5 long, clear pockets. These will need to be taped onto the poster board at both ends and along with bottom, and will need to be sturdy enough to hold five $3^{1}/_{2}$″ square cards each month. Mark the pockets at 4″ intervals and group to give the appearance of 2 ten-frames (plus an extra row).

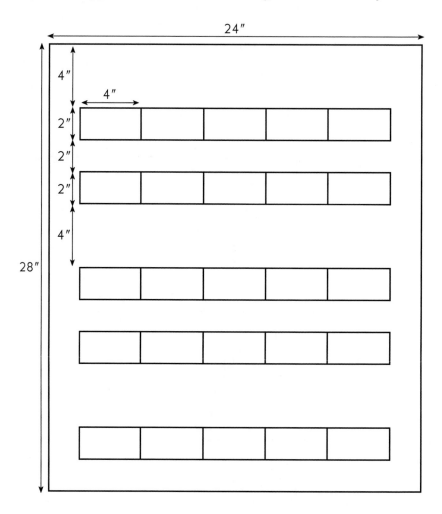

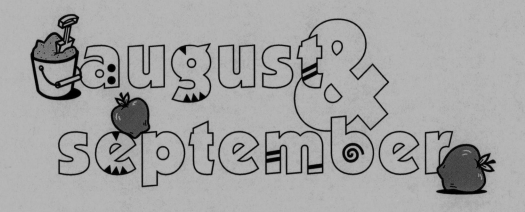

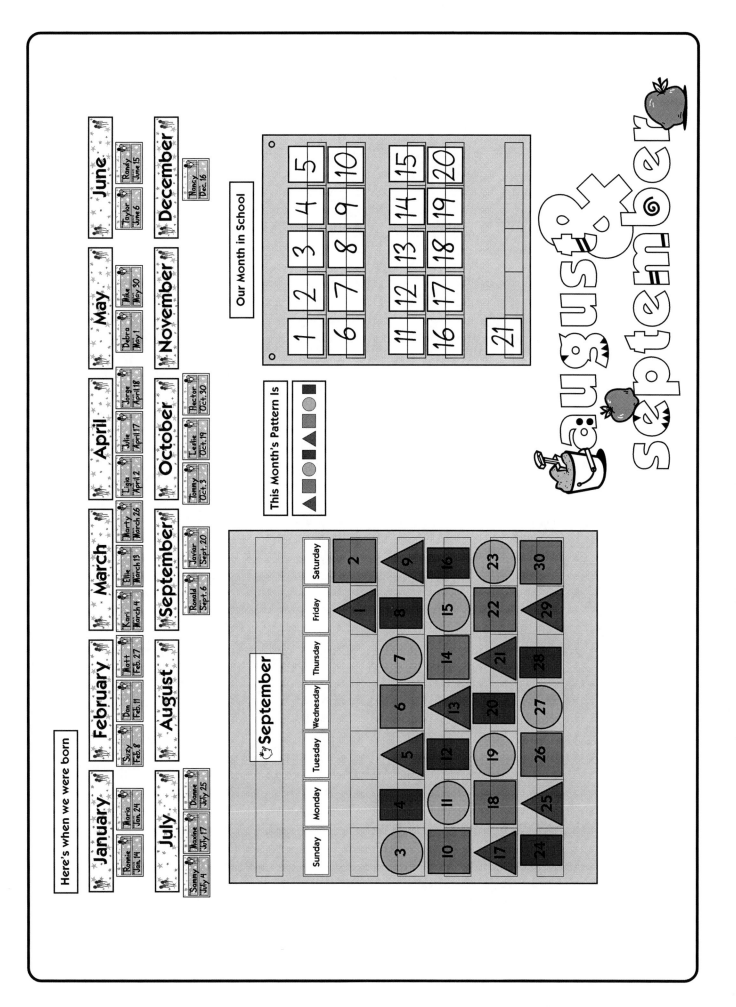

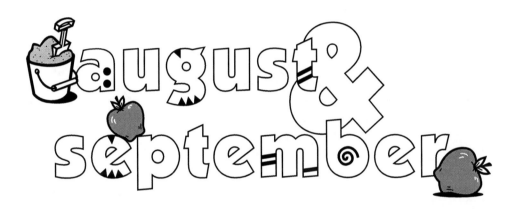

Introduction

Whether your school year begins in August or September, we recommend that you start right away with the Calendar Grid, the Our Month in School chart, and the Here's When We Were Born chart. It will take about 20 minutes a day for the first four days of school to introduce these routines. Knowing how challenging the first week of school is, we suggest that you let these introductory lessons comprise the whole of your math instruction for the first four days of school. By the fifth day, the Number Corner routines will start to feel familiar, and you'll move through them much more quickly. At this point, you can move into the lessons in the *Bridges* Guide or any other math program you might be using. The Number Corner Daily Routines, which should compress to 5 or 10 minutes a day for the rest of the month, might then become a part of your math period or be conducted at another time of the day. (Once they've established the Number Corner routines each month, many teachers use them as part of a daily opening, or even a way to bring each day to a close.) In October the cycle will begin again, as you take another four days to introduce your students to a new set of Daily Routines.

The Calendar Grid

The pattern of markers on the Calendar Grid for August and September features 4 shapes: triangle, square, circle, and rectangle, arranged in an ABCDABCD pattern. Much of your instruction the first four days of school will revolve around these shapes and the sequence in which they're patterned. (If you start school in mid to late August, you'll introduce the pattern then, clear the shapes off the grid at the end of the month, and repeat the same sequence through the month of September. If you teach in a year-round school, you'll want to take a look at your calendar year and adjust things to fit your needs.)

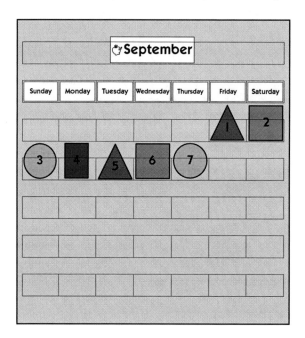

Our Month in School

Children post a new number card in the Our Month in School chart each day they come to school. If you begin school in August, these cards should be removed from the chart at the beginning of September. Start posting number cards anew in September. Be sure to record the number of days in school in August; this number will be needed in October.

Here's When We Were Born

The Here's When We Were Born chart, on which each child's name and birthdate is displayed below the month he or she was born, is something you'll introduce during the first few days of school and refer to periodically throughout the entire year in answer to such perennially favorite questions as: Whose birthdate is next? Who was born in the summer? How many days until my birthdate? Do we have any birthdates coming up this month? Which month has the fewest markers? Which month has the most markers? Were any of our children born on the same day?

Note *If you teach both morning and afternoon sessions of kindergarten, you may want to set up separate charts in your room. The Calendar Grid marker and the Our Month in School daily card can be quickly removed before your second group arrives each day, so you'll only need one of each for both sessions.*

Notes

Day 1

CALENDAR COMPONENTS

Introducing the September Daily Routines

Today's lesson introduces children to two of the three Daily Routines for August and September. Most of the instruction focuses on examining the pattern for the month and learning the four different shapes and their colors. You also enter the first number on the Our Month in School pocket chart.

· ·

The Calendar Grid

Skills

★ learning color names

★ learning shape names

★ describing shapes

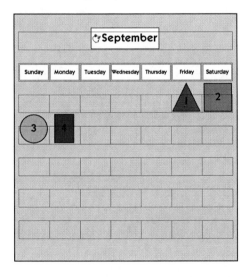

You'll need

★ calendar markers for today and the next 3 days

★ August/September pattern strip

★ small plastic bucket (It helps if the bucket has a fairly wide base.)

★ Shapes song (Poems & Songs Portfolio A, pages PA.1–PA.4. You can bind these pages to make a big book or back them on colored construction or butcher paper to create a wall chart.)

★ helper jar

Open your very first Number Corner lesson by seating children close to your display. When all are settled, call their attention to the calendar grid and the pattern strip for the month. Explain that you'll put up a new marker as each day of the month passes. Their job will be to predict what each day's marker will look like, using the pattern strip to help. (We have written today's lesson with a start date of Tuesday, September 5. If your school year begins in late August or earlier in September, you'll need to modify your instruction accordingly.)

Although there may be children in your class who are able to predict today's shape by examining the markers that have already been posted on the grid, others will need to see the pattern laid out in a straight line, as it is on the pattern strip for the month, in order to make a prediction. The term "pattern"

Day 1 Introducing the September Daily Routines (cont.)

may be brand new to some of your students. The intuitive ideas many preschoolers form about patterns are often limited to ABAB sequences—on, off, on, off; up, down, up, down; red, blue, red, blue—and some of the youngsters in your group may not identify the four-shape sequence as a pattern at all. Nevertheless, there will be an access point for every student in today's lesson. Perhaps it will be simply learning color names, or learning to name and describe shapes. For those who already know the shape and color names, it may be extending the pattern.

After they've had a minute to examine the markers on the calendar grid, ask youngsters to examine the sequence of shapes shown on the pattern strip. What do they notice? (Working with this very open-ended question will give you an opportunity to discover some of the things your children already know about shapes, colors, and patterns.)

Teacher Let's take a look at the strip that shows our calendar pattern. What do you notice?

Children That's pretty.
I like the blue one.
It's the same as the big ones (on the calendar grid).
That yellow one looks like the sun.
It has 1, 2, 3, 4, 5, 6, 7, 8 pieces.
Those are shapes.
I know that blue one. It's like a roof. It's a triangle.
The yellow one is a circle.
I think it's a pattern—we did patterns in my other school.
It keeps going and going.

Building on the observations they've been already made, help students name each of the four shapes pictured on the pattern strip. Then help them use the strip to predict what shape will be posted for today.

Teacher You're doing a great job of noticing lots of things about this pattern. Does anyone know what this red shape is called? (The children have already identified the triangle and the circle, so the teacher directs their attention to the square and the rectangle before moving on.)

Ella I think it's a square. We had that in my other school.

Teacher Do you all agree with Ella?

Day I Introducing the September Daily Routines (cont.)

Children *Maybe.*
Yes!
I don't know.
What's agree?

Teacher *To agree means that you think Ella is right. It is a square. How about this last one, the green one? Do you know what it's called?*

Ella *We had that one in my other school too, but it's hard to remember.*

Deepak *It's sort of like triangle, but I know that's not it.*

Teacher *Good try though. It's called a rectangle. We'll be learning a lot about these shapes this year. Each day this month we're going to add one of these shapes to our calendar. Can you tell what shape we'll need for today?*

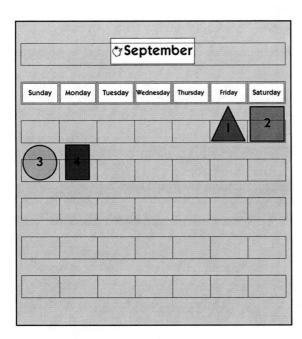

Sammy *It's that blue one! It goes blue, red, yellow, green. It's going to be that blue one again.*

In this class, Sammy has had enough experience with patterns to be able to identify the next marker easily, although he names it by color instead of shape. Perhaps several children in your group will be able to name today's marker by color and shape; perhaps some will be able to select the next shape but not name it; or perhaps no one will be able to answer the question at all, and you'll simply have to tell them. Once the shape that needs to be posted on the grid today has been identified, have the class find it on the pattern strip, name it, and sing the Shapes song verse that applies.

Day I Introducing the September Daily Routines (cont.)

Teacher Sammy's right. We'll need a blue triangle marker for our grid today. Can someone come point to the triangle on our pattern strip?

Children I can, I can. Me too. It's the blue one! Let me do it.

Teacher Since so many people want a turn, I'll pull a name out of the helper jar. I'll shut my eyes and reach in. Let's see. The name on this stick starts with a J. It's Julie! Would you like to come up and point to the triangle?

Teacher Do you agree with Julie? Is that one a triangle?

Children It's blue. She's right. I don't know. I never heard about triangles before.

Teacher I have a simple song that will help us learn about triangles. I'll sing it to you and then you can sing along with me the second time. It has same tune as "Row, Row, Row Your Boat."

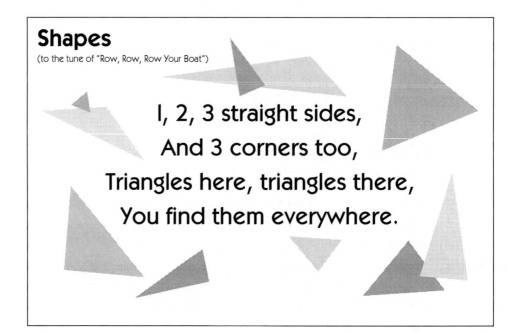

Shapes
(to the tune of "Row, Row, Row Your Boat")

I, 2, 3 straight sides,
And 3 corners too,
Triangles here, triangles there,
You find them everywhere.

Day 1 Introducing the September Daily Routines (cont.)

After singing the appropriate Shapes song verse, take a moment to reexamine the shape on the pattern strip. How many sides does it have? How many corners? Then show children the shape for today, along with the shapes for the next three days. Place them in your plastic bucket and select a helper to close her eyes, reach into the bucket, and find today's shape by touch. Encourage your group to think about the properties the helper will need to consider in order to do this task.

Teacher *Here's today's shape, along with the shapes we'll need for the next three days. I'm going to mix them up and put them in the bucket. I'll pull another stick out of the helper jar and ask that person to close his or her eyes and reach into the bucket to pull out the triangle. What will our helper need to think about to find the right shape?*

Children *It has to be pointy.*
It won't be round.
It has to have 3 of those straight parts.
It has to be blue.
Does the helper get to peek?

Teacher *No, the helper can't peek. Will the helper be able to feel the pointed corners?*

Children *Yes.*

Teacher *How many corners and sides will he or she need to count?*

Children *3!*

Teacher *Here goes—the stick says Javiar. Can you come and reach in the bucket and try to figure out which one of these shapes has 3 sides and 3 corners?*

Once the shape has been pulled out of the bucket, post it on the calendar grid. Then draw children's attention to the name of the day on the grid and read it to them (Tuesday, in this case).

Day 1 Introducing the September Daily Routines (cont.)

. . . .

Our Month in School

Skills

★ counting

★ recognizing numerals

★ writing numerals

You'll need

★ 3½" × 3½" square of white cardstock

★ black wide-tipped marking pen

★ chalkboard and chalk *or* white board and pen

★ Our Month in School pocket chart

You'll want to finish today's session quickly since this has been a long time for many kindergartners to persevere. Draw their attention to the Our Month in School chart and explain that for this entire month you'll be inserting a number card each day they come to school.

After you've established the fact that it's going to be a "1" today because they've only been in school one day, model how to write the numeral 1 on your chalkboard or white board, have them copy you by writing on the rug or in the air with their fingers (their "skywriters"), and then record the numeral on a blank square cut to fit the chart.

> **Teacher** *We have another job to do quickly. How many days have you come to kindergarten?*
>
> **Children** *1.*
> *This is our first day!*
>
> **Teacher** *This month we'll keep track of how many days we come to school by putting a number in a pocket on this chart each morning/afternoon. Today, I'll need to write a 1, and here's how.* (The teacher models writing a 1 on the chalkboard.) *Can you write a 1 for me in the air? Good! Now I'll write it on our pocket chart card. I'll start it at the top and make a straight line just like you did.*

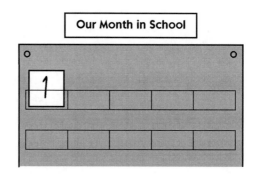

Day 2

CALENDAR COMPONENTS

Introducing the September Daily Routines

Today's lesson is like yesterday's, focusing first on the calendar grid, and then briefly on the Our Month in School and Here's When We Were Born charts.

. . . .

The Calendar Grid

Skills
★ learning color names
★ learning shape names
★ describing shapes

You'll need
★ calendar markers for today and the next 3 days
★ August/September pattern strip
★ a small plastic bucket
★ Shapes song
★ helper jar

Ask children to sit on the floor or rug in front of your Number Corner display board, and then have them look at the pattern strip. Review the shape names and read the pattern together. We recommend that you read it twice, naming the colors the second time rather than the shapes, so students who don't yet know or may be confused by the shape names have access to the pattern too.

Teacher *What do you remember about the shapes on our pattern strip?*

Children *That first one is a triangle.*
Then there's a square and a circle.
What's that next one?

Teacher *That's called a rectangle. You're doing a great job naming the shapes. Let me pull out a helper stick and the helper can point to each of the shapes in our pattern as we name them.*

After the children have named each of the shapes, ask the helper to point to each of them once again as you read the pattern by color. Then work with students to identify which of the shapes in the sequence you used on the calendar grid yesterday, and which one you'll need today. Once they've deter-

Day 2 Introducing the September Daily Routines (cont.)

mined what today's shape will be, take a minute to sing the appropriate verse of the Shapes song and discuss the properties of this shape.

Teacher *What shape did we put on the calendar yesterday?*

Children *The blue one.*
The pointy one.
The triangle.
I found it in the bucket.
It has a 5 on it.

Teacher *It sounds like everyone agrees that the shape we added to the calendar grid yesterday was a blue triangle. I'll get a stick from the jar for a new helper to point to the next shape on our pattern strip. Kari, it's you. Will you come and point to the shape that comes after the triangle?*

Teacher *What do we call this shape?*

Children *It's red.*
It's the square, I remember from my other school.

Teacher *Our Shapes song has some more verses. Let's sing the one that will help us learn about squares. I'll sing it to you and then you can sing along with me the second time.*

After singing the appropriate Shapes song verse, take a moment to reexamine today's shape on the pattern strip. How many sides does it have? How many corners? Then show children the shape for today, along with the shapes for the next three days. Place all four shapes in your plastic bucket and select a helper to close her eyes, reach into the bucket, and find today's shape by touch. Notice that in the discussion below, the teacher asks children to think about how the helper will be able to feel the shape she needs (a square, in this case). This question encourages students to describe the needed shape in greater detail than they might otherwise. The teacher then asks how the helper will know that the shape she's feeling is a square rather than a rectangle, thereby stimulating children to observe and describe the differences between the two shapes.

Day 2 Introducing the September Daily Routines (cont.)

Teacher *I'm going to mix up all 4 shapes and put them in the bucket. I'll pull out 1 more helper stick and ask that person to close his or her eyes and reach into the bucket to pull out the square. What will our helper need to think about to find the right shape?*

Children *It's like a box.*
It's red.
4 sides.
4 corners!

Teacher *This is going to be mighty tricky. How will the helper know it's a square and not a rectangle?*

Children *She can just guess.*
She can put it back if she gets it wrong.
If it's not red, it's not the square.

Teacher *Is there anything else about a square our helper should know before he or she reaches in? The song says the sides are the same. What does that mean?*

Children *They're not so long.*
They're all kind of short.
They're the same size.

If the helper pulls out the wrong shape, leave that one out of the bucket and encourage her to try again. Once the shape has been found, post it in the appropriate pocket on the calendar grid. Then draw children's attention to the name of the day on the grid and read it to them (Wednesday, in this case).

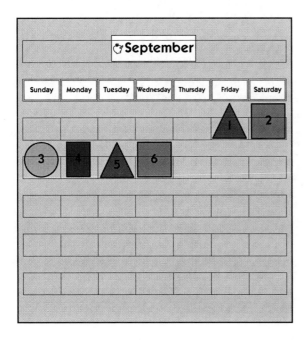

Day 2 Introducing the September Daily Routines (cont.)

. . . .

Our Month in School

Skills

★ counting

★ recognizing numerals

★ writing numerals

You'll need

★ 3½" × 3½" square of white cardstock

★ black wide-tipped marking pen

★ Our Month in School pocket chart

★ chalkboard and chalk *or* white board and pen

Once the correct marker has been posted on the calendar grid, take a minute or two to create a new card for the chart. This is a good opportunity to show children what the numeral 2 looks like and how to write it correctly. Although it's early in the year for most to be working with chalk or pencils, children will benefit from "writing" on the rug or in the air with their fingers.

Teacher We have another job to do quickly. Yesterday was the first day of school. Today is another day. I have to write a new number to show how many days we've been in school. What should I write?

Children You have to write a 2.

Teacher Good job! Let me show you on my white board how to write a 2. You have to start at the top and go around like this and then give it a straight line at the bottom. I'll write another one. You see if you can write it with your finger on the rug. Good job! Try it again. Now I'll write a 2 on this card and put it on our chart.

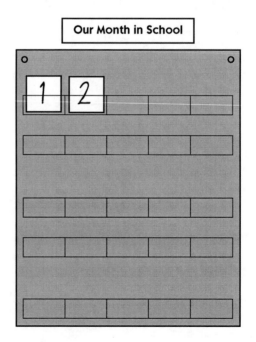

Day 2 Introducing the September Daily Routines (cont.)

. . . .

Here's When We Were Born

Skills

★ learning the names of the months

★ reading names

You'll need

★ Here's When We Were Born markers (Blackline NC I, run enough copies to create a marker for each student. Post each child's marker under his or her birth month. See instructions on page 18.)

Conclude your Number Corner lesson for today by talking about birthdates. Does anyone have a birthdate today? Children will certainly want to tell you if they've had a birthdate recently. You're almost sure to hear about upcoming birthdates and parties as well. You may have a fair number of students who don't know when their birthdates are, however. Assure them that the Here's When We Were Born chart in the Number Corner will let everyone know about all the birthdates in class. Read through the twelve months of the year and show children that you've posted a marker for each of them under their birth month.

Then point to the current month (August or September) and read the names of the children on the markers below. Does anyone have a birthdate today? Did anyone have a birthdate earlier in the month, before school started? How many children were born this month?

Day 3

CALENDAR COMPONENTS

Introducing the September Daily Routines

Children figure out which shape belongs on the calendar grid and learn a song about the days of the week. Also, they record the number of days they have been in school so far and take another look at the Here's When We Were Born chart.

. . . .

The Calendar Grid

Skills

★ naming and describing basic shapes

★ exploring patterns

★ recognizing numerals

★ learning the names of the days

You'll need

★ calendar markers for today and the next 3 days

★ August/September pattern strip

★ small plastic bucket

★ Shapes song

★ helper jar

★ "Days of the Week" song (You'll find this song on the cassette tape or CD, *Songs for Number Corner by Greg and Steve*)

After gathering students to your Number Corner, open the session by asking children to discuss the calendar pattern. If you ask this in an open-ended way, the question will give you a chance to discover whether or not your children, as a group, can name the shapes and colors, and what they understand about the nature of the pattern itself. Then ask students to think about what would come next if the pattern were to continue on and on, beyond what they can see on the strip. Finally, have them identify today's shape.

> **Teacher** *What do you remember about our calendar pattern?*
>
> **Children** *That first one is a triangle.*
> *Then there's a square and a circle.*
> *Oh, oh! That green one is hard. I know, it's like a wreck—when your car gets smashed. Rectangle!*
>
> **Teacher** *That was some clever problem solving you did to figure that one out. I need a helper. Here's a helper stick and the name starts with L. Raise your hand if you think it might be you. Ligia? You're right!*

Day 3 Introducing the September Daily Routines (cont.)

Your name is the only one in our class that starts with L. Will you come and point to our pattern while we read the whole thing? What if we wanted to just keep going and going with the same pattern? What would come after the green rectangle?

Dianna *I like the yellow one. Let's put that next.*

Amy *Red is my best color. I'm wearing red. Let's do red.*

Deepak *But that wouldn't be the same pattern. You can't change it.*

Kari *I think it has to start again with the blue one.*

Children *Yes, the triangle.*
You can't do the yellow one first. It comes after the red one, not after the green one.

Teacher *It sounds like we'll need to keep adding markers to our calendar for awhile in order to be absolutely certain how this pattern works. What shape will we need today?*

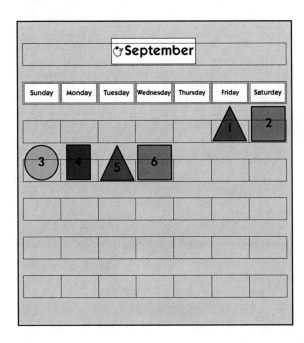

Ella *We used the red one yesterday. It'll be the yellow one today.*

Teacher *Let's have a look at our pattern strip. Jesse, will you point to the shape that comes after the red square? It's the third one. What shape is that?*

Day 3 Introducing the September Daily Routines (cont.)

Children It's yellow. It's the round one. Circle! It's a circle all right. That will be easy to find in the bucket. Can I do it?

Once children have determined which shape they'll need for the calendar grid today, sing the appropriate Shapes song verse. Place today's marker, along with the three that follow, in the plastic bucket and ask children to name some of the things a helper might consider in order to pull the correct shape out by touch alone. Then choose a helper to find the shape by feel and post it on the calendar grid.

Finally, introduce the "Days of the Week" song. This delightful song, found on *Songs for Number Corner by Greg and Steve*, takes about a minute to sing, and simply sets the names of the days, along with one other verse, to a bouncy little tune. It's an easy way to teach children the names of the days and their sequence. Once they've learned the song, you can use it to help students identify the name of the day on the calendar grid. For today, however, just playing the recorded version and then inviting children to sing along a second time will be sufficient. When you're finished, show them the name of the day on the calendar grid and read it together.

. . . .

Our Month in School

Skills

★ counting

★ recognizing numerals

★ writing numerals

You'll need

★ 3½" × 3½" square of white cardstock

★ black wide-tipped marking pen

★ Our Month in School pocket chart

★ chalkboard and chalk *or* white board and pen

Once you've posted the day's marker and identified the day of the week, take a minute or two to create a new card for the Our Month in School pocket chart. As you do so, show children what the numeral 3 looks like and how to write it correctly, and have them practice in the air or on the rug with their imaginary writing tools.

Teacher What's our next job in the Number Corner? Do you remember?

Children We have to put another card with those others—the ones that say 1, 2.
How many days we've been here.

Day 3 Introducing the September Daily Routines (cont.)

Teacher *That's right. We have to add another card to our Our Month in School chart. How many days have we been coming to school?*

Children *3 comes next.*
It goes 1, 2, 3.

Teacher *You're right. This is our third day in school, and we'll need to add a 3 to our chart.*

. . . .

Here's When We Were Born

Finally, take another look at the Here's When We Were Born chart. Does anyone have a birthdate today? Are there any markers at all posted for the month? What about next month? If it's going to be a few weeks or more until the next birthdate comes along, you might want to set this routine aside for now.

Day 4

 CALENDAR COMPONENTS

Introducing the September Daily Routines

This lesson jumps ahead to consider what might happen if you miss a few days of Number Corner instruction. In this case, the teacher skipped Friday because there were other things to do and then the weekend intervened. Now children are working on Monday to bring things up to date.

. . . .

The Calendar Grid

Skills
★ naming and describing basic shapes

★ exploring patterns

★ recognizing numerals

★ learning the names of the days

You'll need
★ calendar markers for today and any days that have been missed—make sure you include all 4 shapes in the collection

★ August/September pattern strip

★ a small plastic bucket

★ Shapes song

★ helper jar

★ Days of the Week song

Any time you've been away from the Number Corner for more than a day or two, you'll want to take a few minutes to review the pattern on the pattern strip, and then work with children to determine which marker belongs in each of the pockets until the calendar grid has been brought up to date. If your class has missed the opportunity to work with one of the shapes, as is the case here, you'll want to be sure to sing the appropriate verse of the Shapes song and have them discuss the properties of this shape. As several days have gone by, more than one child will have the opportunity to pull a shape out of the bucket.

> **Teacher** *Oh, oh! It has been a few days since we met in the Number Corner. What was the last shape we put on our calendar grid?*
>
> **Children** *The round one.*
> *The yellow circle!*
>
> **Teacher** *We got busy on Friday and didn't have a chance to put up our calendar marker. What should have come right after the yellow circle on Friday? Take a look at the shapes on the pattern strip and tell a friend what you think.*

Day 4 Introducing the September Daily Routines (cont.)

Encourage children to discuss their ideas with one another. Though not all students will understand what you mean when you say, "Tell a friend what you think," it's an important instructional technique to use all year long. If your youngsters don't have any idea how to begin, take a moment to role-play how to "tell a friend" with some of your more verbal students.

> **Teacher** *You've had a moment to talk it over. What do you think?*

> **Children** *It's a green one. A rectangle. We think it's the blue one. Is it red?*

> **Deepak** *It can't be blue or red. That wouldn't be in our pattern. It has to be the green rectangle. Look at our pattern up there and you can tell. The green rectangle always comes after the yellow circle.*

> **Teacher** *That's an interesting idea. Deepak says that the green rectangle always comes after the yellow circle. What do you think of that? Deepak, how about if you come up and point while we read the pattern on the strip? We'll try to keep it going even after we can't see it any more.*

Have children read the pattern as a helper points. Ask them to continue naming shapes beyond the ones they can see on the strip. Does everyone agree that the rectangle comes after the circle every time? They won't all understand yet, but by the end of the month, with more opportunities to explore repeating patterns, many of your children will be more confident.

After some discussion about the pattern itself, put the next four shapes in the bucket and use the helper jar to choose children to pull them out for the days that need to be filled on the calendar grid.

Day 4 Introducing the September Daily Routines (cont.)

If one of the markers is a shape your class hasn't yet discussed, you may want to sing the appropriate verse of the Shapes song and discuss its attributes in the context of giving the helper some clues to feel for as she reaches into the bucket.

Teacher *Maxine, I've picked your stick. Will you please pull the rectangle out of the bucket? What are some of the things that might help Maxine's fingers feel the rectangle when she reaches into the bucket?*

Ella *That's going to be hard. She might get it mixed up with the square when she tries to find it.*

Sammy *She could take the square out if she gets it and try again.*

Ronak *That green one isn't fat like the square. If she finds one with 4 corners, she has to see if it's fat everywhere. If it is, she has to find the one that's not fat everywhere.*

Teacher *Maxine, the children have made some good suggestions, but I'm not sure I could find the rectangle on the first try either. There's 1 more verse to our shapes song. Let's sing it before you try to pull that rectangle out of the bucket.*

Children *She did it!*

Teacher *That was really amazing. How do you think she did that?*

Children *It was magic.*
She feeled it.
She looked for the fat and skinny one that wasn't round.
She didn't get the one with 3 sides.

Teacher *All right! Now we need to put up the markers for Saturday, Sunday, and Monday. I need another helper. Maria, I pulled your stick out of the jar. Please come and point to the next shape we need to keep our pattern going.*

Day 4 Introducing the September Daily Routines (cont.)

Children *The blue one.*
The triangle.
That's easy.
I want to be the helper.

Teacher *Here goes—how will Maria be able to feel the triangle?*

Children *It will have 3 points—3 straight sides too.*
What do you call those?
I know, corners—3 corners.
Yep! She got it!

Continue asking helpers to pull shapes out of the bucket until your calendar grid has been brought up to date. Then run through the "Days of the Week" song with your class. This time, point to the days on the calendar grid as they're named in the song. When you're finished singing, point to the calendar marker last posted. Can the children figure out the name of that day? If not, give them a hand.

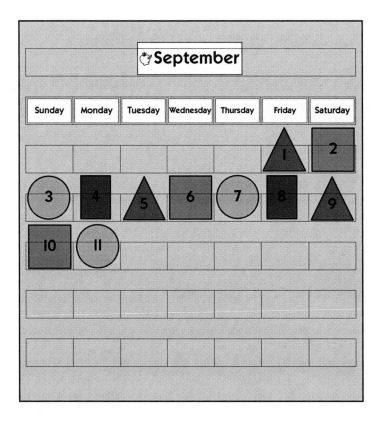

Day 4 Introducing the September Daily Routines (cont.)

. . . .

Our Month in School

Skills

★ counting

★ recognizing numerals

★ writing numerals

You'll need

★ 3½" × 3½" square of white cardstock

★ black wide-tipped marking pen

★ Our Month in School pocket chart

★ chalkboard and chalk or white board and pen

Once you've finished putting the new markers on the calendar grid, take a few minutes to update the Our Month in School chart. This task will be more complex than usual as children will have to consider the fact that they weren't in school over the weekend. Students may also experience some confusion between the number of days that have passed in the month so far and the number of days they've come to school.

> **Teacher** *How many days have you been in kindergarten?*
>
> **Children** *Lots!*
> *There are lots of shapes on the calendar—11.*
> *But we weren't here some of those days. We watched cartoons on Saturday. I went to my Grandma's house on Sunday.*
> *But there are 11 things up there.*
> *But we only get to write a number for when we're at school.*
> *It's 5, 'cause last time it was 3, and now it's 4, 5.*
>
> **Teacher** *It's true that our calendar grid shows 11 days, but you're right about only being in school 5 of those days. We didn't start school until September 5th, and we didn't come to school on Saturday or Sunday. We'll need to make cards that say 4 and 5 for our Our Month in School chart.*

Even though a discussion like the one above may not make sense to all of your students right now, they'll have repeated opportunities to sort things out over the coming months. For many of your children the immediate value of this lesson will revolve around counting, numeral recognition, and numeral formation. Demonstrate how to write the needed numbers while children practice "writing" them on the rug or in the air. Then record the numbers on cards and post them on your chart.

Day 5

CALENDAR COMPONENTS

Continuing Through September

Now that you've introduced the Daily Routines for August and September, you can move through them much more quickly. We suggest that you aim to hold your Number Corner sessions to 5 to 10 minutes a day, 3 or 4 days a week. You can shorten your instruction some days by limiting the discussions you hold about the shapes, or eliminating the step of reaching into the bucket to find the shape. There may be times when you decide to sing the Days of the Week song and other times you don't. You may keep the Shapes song on display but sing it only occasionally. Numeral writing may be part of the Our Month in School routine some days, but not always. Here's When We Were Born need only come up for occasional discussion.

As you shift the bulk of your math instruction to the lessons in the *Bridges* Guide (or another math program) you'll find that there are days you don't have time to get to the Number Corner at all. On these days, you may want to have a student post the calendar marker, or you may want to engage children in playing "catch-up" the following day.

Here are some ideas to consider in shaping your instruction during the 3 or 4 days a week you do use the Number Corner routines. Emphasize *one or two* of the skills/concepts listed for each of the three routines whenever you conduct a Number Corner session with your class.

. . . .

The Calendar Grid

Focus on helping children:
- make predictions about the shapes that will be added to the grid, using the pattern strip to help.
- understand that one type of pattern is something that repeats over and over.
- understand that because patterns repeat, we can use them to make predictions.

Day 5 Continuing Through September (cont.)

- name and describe the four shapes as they're added to the calendar grid. (Singing the entire Shapes song or selected verses is a nice way to review the properties of the four shapes you introduced at the beginning of the month.)

Round and round
And round and round,
No corners can you see,
Like the sun and the moon,
Circles are everywhere.

Our Month in School

Focus on helping children:
- count one by one and read numerals
- practice numeral formation using skywriting or rug-writing
- recall the names of numerals

Here's When We Were Born

Focus on helping children:
- read the names of any classmates who have birthdates coming up in the near future.

october

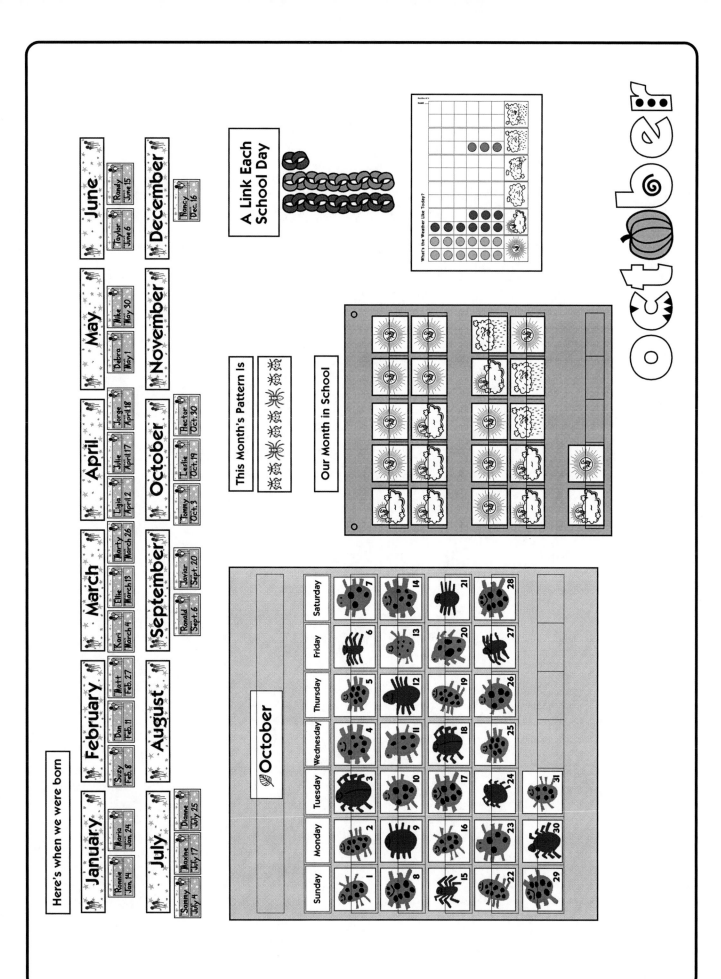

Introduction

A month or more of school has passed. By now, you and your students have probably become comfortable with the Daily Routines. In October, all three routines—the Calendar Grid, Our Month in School, and Here's When We Were Born—continue with one addition and a few changes. As at the beginning of the school year, it will probably take three or four full math periods to make the shifts, which include creating and patterning a new set of calendar markers with your class, introducing a new method of keeping track of how many days you've been in school, and starting to mark the passing school days with weather cards instead of numbers on the Our Month in School chart. Once these changes have been effected, the Daily Routines will compress again to 5 or 10 minutes a day, and you'll be able to return to the lessons in the *Bridges* Guide or another math program you're using. In November the cycle will begin again, as you phase into yet another set of modifications in the Daily Routines.

A Link Each School Day Building a Yearlong Paper Chain

To open the new month, you'll work with your students to count the number cards that were collected in the Our Month in School chart during September. Then the children will help create a paper chain to reflect the total, each link standing for a single day in school, and the color of the links alternating every ten. (If you started school in August, be sure to include the number of days that children attended school that month in your chain.) This will be the beginning of a Yearlong Paper Chain, to which you'll add at the end of each month and which will eventually show the total number of days the children have spent in kindergarten.

The Calendar Grid

This month, children will create the markers for the calendar grid. We like to have our students make construction paper ladybugs and spiders, although you can certainly modify the instructions to have your students make calendar markers to match a different theme. On the second day of the four-lesson sequence, you'll engage children in exploring different ways to create patterns with the markers they made, before choosing the pattern that will go on the calendar grid. As in September, you'll display the chosen pattern on a strip next to the grid to help children make predictions about the markers that will be posted each day.

Our Month in School

During the lesson on Day 2, you'll also introduce a new set of markers for the Our Month in School chart. These are a set of six weather cards depicting the following weather conditions: sunny, partly sunny, cloudy, windy, rainy, and snowy.

Each day they come to school this month, children will determine what the prevailing weather condition is and post the appropriate card in the Our Month in School chart. They'll also mark the weather on a paper graph so that by the end of the month, they'll have a record of the daily weather conditions in October.

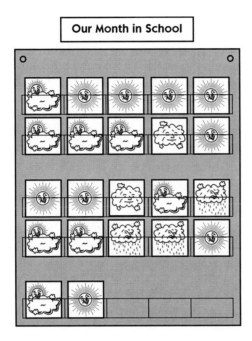

Our Month in School

By the fourth or fifth day of October, you and your students will have made and patterned the new markers, become familiar with the weather cards for the Our Month in School chart, learned how to graph the weather, started a new paper chain to reflect the number of school days in October, and discussed the Here's When We Were Born chart at least once. You'll need 20 to 40 minutes each day to make these changes in the Daily Routines, but by the fifth or sixth day these routines will only require 5 to 10 minutes a day and you'll have time to return to the Problems & Investigations lessons in the *Bridges* Guide, along with the Work Places.

Notes

Day 1

CALENDAR COMPONENTS

Introducing the October Daily Routines

Before the September calendar disappears, children revisit the Our Month in School chart to determine how many days they've been coming to kindergarten so far this year. After counting the cards in the chart, they work with you to create a paper chain with as many links as days they came to school in September. (If school began for you in August, you need to also add the number of links needed to maintain an accurate history of the days children have attended kindergarten.) This paper chain is hung in a convenient place in the room so that at the end of each month more links can be added. The other thing children do today is make calendar markers for the new month—bugs this time, in keeping with the theme coming up in *Bridges* of spiders, butterflies, ladybugs, and other favorite bug friends.

. . . .

Note If you plan to study something other than bugs in October, feel free to adapt the instructions on pages 58–60 so children can make calendar markers that will better fit your theme. We do encourage you to have students participate in making the markers, however, because they tend to be more interested in the Number Corner when their art work is displayed on the calendar grid. Having them create the markers also allows children to take a part in changing the display, rather than having the September calendar disappear mysteriously overnight.

. . . .

. . . .

A Link Each School Day Starting the Yearlong Paper Chain

Skills

★ counting by 1's

★ counting by 10's

★ adding "1 more"

You'll need

★ September Number Corner display

★ helper jar

★ 1" × 7" construction paper strips in 2 different colors (10 strips in 1 color and 12 or 13 in another for today's work. Or, cut up 2 entire 12" × 18" sheets, 1 in each color, to use as needed.)

★ glue

Open the session by seating children close to your display. When everyone is settled, tell them that a new month has started. Some of them may be aware of this, because of approaching birthdays or other eagerly anticipated events.

Day I Introducing the October Daily Routines (cont.)

Explain that, because October has arrived, you'll be working together to change some things on the calendar. Before you can do this, though, they'll need to figure out how many days they've already been in kindergarten so they can make a paper chain to keep track all year long of the days they've been kindergartners. Where could they find that information? Some may look on the calendar grid and conclude that they've been in school for 30 days, while others will remember that it's the number cards on the Our Month in School chart that indicate how many days they've come to school. Once they've determined this, help them count the cards in the Our Month in School chart by 1's, and then 5's.

> **Teacher** *Before we take down the September calendar markers and change the Our Month in School chart, we need to figure out how many school days have passed already. How could we find that out?*

> **Children** *That's easy! Look at those numbers. We can just count. I can read it. It says 30. But the other one says 21. I think you can't do the 30—that's some days we didn't come. Let's count on the blue chart with the numbers. 1, 2, 3, 4, 5, 6, 7, 8, 9, 10, 11, 12, 13, 14, 15, 16, 17, 18, 19, 20, 21! It's 21 all right!*

> **Teacher** *It sounds like you've figured that out correctly. Is there any other way to count the number cards?*

> **Marco** *We could do it faster.*

> **Teacher** *That's true. I'm wondering if you've ever heard anyone count by 5's or by 10's?*

Day 1 Introducing the October Daily Routines (cont.)

Suzy My brother can do that really fast. I already know some of it.

Teacher Let's take a look at the Our Month in School chart and I'll help you begin learning how to count by 5's.

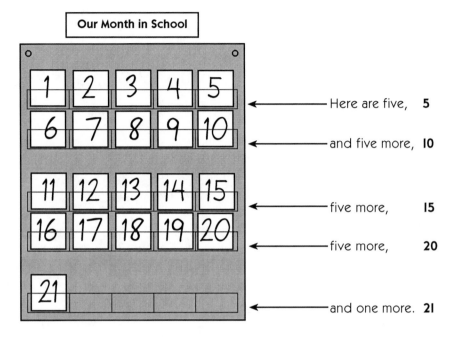

Teacher We get to go to school 180 days this year, and I'd like to keep track of how many days have passed by making a paper chain with a loop for every day we've been in school. We'll make the first 10 loops the same color. I'll pick a helper stick from the jar in a few minutes so we can get some paper loops made, but first let me show you how to do this.

Demonstrate how to form a loop with the paper strip and put a line of glue across the end. Hold the loop together while everyone counts to twenty so the glue can adhere. Add a second loop by hooking it through the first. How many loops are there now?

Continue quickly adding loops with the help of a new student each time until you get to ten and then change to a second color. When you've put on the second ten, change back to the first color. How many loops are there altogether?

Teacher Let's count how many loops are in our chain now. I'll need another helper who can touch each loop as we count.

Guide children to count the loop by 1's. Then point out that each of the two color groups has ten. Explain that they will be adding more loops to this chain at the end of each month and counting them many times as the school year goes along. Have students help you find a special place in the room to hang this chain.

Day 1 Introducing the October Daily Routines (cont.)

· ·

The Calendar Grid Making the New Markers

Skills

★ gathering information from text

★ observing and describing

You'll need

★ Ladybird Beetle song (Poems & Songs Portfolio A, pages PA.5–PA.10, create a wall chart or big book)

★ Spider song (Poems & Songs Portfolio A, pages PA.11–PA.15, create a wall chart or big book)

★ scissors, glue, and pencils

★ 5" × 5" white construction paper squares on which to mount ladybugs and spiders

To make ladybugs

★ 3" × 3" squares of red construction paper (20 or more)

★ 2" × 3" pieces of black construction paper (20 or more)

★ 2" × 2" squares of black construction paper (20 or more)

★ ¼" × 3" black strips (lots for legs and antennae)

To make spiders

★ 3" × 3" squares of brown construction paper (20 or more)

★ 2" × 2" squares of brown construction paper (20 or more)

★ ¼" × 3" brown strips (lots for legs)

Now that the September days in school have been noted and recorded, it's time to make calendar markers for the new month. You might want to introduce the theme of bugs with a song, a fingerplay, or a favorite short story. We've included two songs in the blacklines that offer lots of information about ladybugs and spiders in a rhythmic and playful way. Even if you don't choose to use them today, keep both songs around this month. If you're using the entire *Bridges* program, you'll find additional suggestions for studying ladybugs, spiders, and ants in Bugs Across the Curriculum (*Bridges*, Volume One).

Ladybird Beetle
(to the tune of "Are You Sleeping?")

Ladybird beetle, ladybird beetle,
Red with black spots, red with black spots,

You help us in our gardens
Eating lots of aphids,

Three body parts, three body parts.

Day 1 Introducing the October Daily Routines (cont.)

After a short song or story break, gather everyone in a "U" or a circle to model how to make a ladybug or a spider using the construction paper you cut. (Although you won't need all of them for the calendar grid, it would be ideal to wind up with at least 20 spiders and 20 ladybugs. If you teach two sessions of kindergarten, you might want to have one class make the ladybugs and the other class make the spiders. If you only have one group, you'll probably want to have a few of the students who work more quickly make both a spider and a ladybug.)

> *Teacher* *Do you remember from our Spider song how many body parts they have?*

> *Hector* *I know about spiders. They have a head and the other part. What do you call it?*

> *Teacher* *Does anyone remember that part of the song?*

> *Julie* *I think it's their tummy part.*

> *Teacher* *You're very close. The song calls that part the "abdomen" and it's a little bigger than the head and chest part. Do you see these 2 sizes of paper? I'll use the bigger piece to make the abdomen. I have to draw a circle, but it doesn't have to be perfect. I need to make it as big as I can so anyone that comes into our room will be able to see our spiders and ladybugs on the calendar. When I cut it out, I have to remember to turn the paper. If you have any trouble cutting, ask a friend to help you. I only need a little glue to hook these together. Now for some legs. Let's see, how many legs do spiders have?*

> *Children* *8! 8 hairy legs! 4 on each side. I know that 4 + 4 makes 8.*

Once you've demonstrated how to make the paper spiders, have children take a quick stretch and then show them how to make the ladybugs, as illustrated below. Finally, send them out to work on their own. You'll need to wind up with 31 bugs in all for the calendar grid. If one bug is much more popular than the other, that's okay, but try to encourage children to choose in such a way that you have at least 10 of one and 21 of the other by the time they're finished. (If you have two sessions, this should be easy. Extra bugs can be sent home later or used for decoration elsewhere in the room.)

Day 1 Introducing the October Daily Routines (cont.)

As they finish their work, help students put their names on the backs of their bugs and find safe places for them to dry. Although some children will beg to take their bugs home at the end of today's class, be sure to save them. You'll need all the bugs for tomorrow's Number Corner lesson and at least 31 of them for the calendar grid.

Day 2

 CALENDAR COMPONENTS

Introducing the October Daily Routines

The markers are ready. What pattern would be most interesting on this month's calendar grid? Today, children form several different patterns. After you choose one of these, post and number the first few markers to bring the October calendar up to date. Then children check on current weather conditions and post that information (along with yesterday's weather) on the Our Month in School chart.

. . . .

The Calendar Grid What Shall Our Pattern Be?

Skills

★ copying and extending repeating patterns

★ exploring AB, AABB, AAB, and ABB patterns

You'll need

★ calendar grid with the September markers removed

★ ladybugs and spiders students made yesterday

★ October pattern strips

★ pocket chart

★ Calendar Numbers, sheets 1–2 (Black-lines NC 2–NC 3, run 1 copy of each and cut apart)

Invite children to join you in the discussion area. Explain that they're going to work together to make some patterns with their bugs before you choose one for the class calendar grid. Pass out the ladybugs and spiders, one per child. If the class made both kinds, return each bug to its owner. If you teach two sessions, explain that you want this month's calendar grid to feature both spiders and ladybugs, which means that some children might end up holding bugs that were made by students in the other class.

After the bugs have been distributed, display one of your pattern strips in the pocket chart and read the sequence together.

Can the children, holding their ladybugs and spiders, stand in a line that will match this pattern? Call them up a few at a time to form the pattern. Con-

Day 2 Introducing the October Daily Routines (cont.)

tinue until everyone is standing. Is it still the same pattern? Have everyone chant the pattern as a helper points to each person in the line.

Then ask everyone to sit down again. Post another strip and read the new pattern together. To copy the pattern, how many ladybugs will they need? (4) spiders? (4). Call children up again a few at a time to form a line that matches and then extends this pattern. When everyone is standing, chant the pattern together as a new helper points to each child in the line.

Continue in this manner until you've explored three or perhaps all four of the patterns shown on the strips, and then choose one to use on your calendar grid. (If you have at least 21 ladybugs or spiders in your collection, you might want to choose one of the two patterns shown below because both of them create such interesting diagonals as they develop throughout the month. If you don't have enough ladybugs or spiders, choose one of the first two patterns to go on the grid.)

Collect all the bugs from your students. Post enough of the bugs on the grid to bring the calendar up to date. Post the strip that shows the chosen pattern.

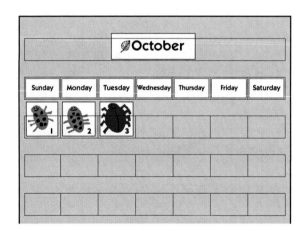 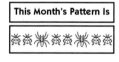

Once the bugs have been placed in the correct calendar pockets, ask children what numeral should be placed on each. With the children's guidance, glue the Calendar Marker Numbers on the appropriate bugs.

Day 2 Introducing the October Daily Routines (cont.)

Our Month in School

Skills

★ observing and describing the weather

You'll need

★ Our Month in School chart with the number cards from September removed

★ Weather cards

Next, draw children's attention to the Our Month in School chart. Explain that this month, instead of writing numbers each day they come to school, they'll be checking on the outside weather and recording their observations by placing a card on the chart. Show them a sample of each weather card and then go outside to check on current weather conditions. Which picture best fits today's weather? What was the weather like yesterday? Which picture best shows yesterday's conditions?

Select a helper to post the two cards needed to bring the Our Month in School chart up to date.

Day 3

 CALENDAR COMPONENTS

Introducing the October Daily Routines

Now that the calendar markers have been made, the pattern established, and the weather cards introduced, the Daily Routines start to settle into a more familiar groove. Today, children post a new marker on the calendar grid after making predictions. Then they go outside to check the weather. When they come in, they vote on which of the weather cards best shows the day's weather conditions. The picture most students select is posted on the Our Month in School chart. Finally, help students start a paper chain for October that shows how many days they've come to school this month. At the end of the month, this chain is added to the Yearlong Paper Chain.

. . . .

The Calendar Grid What Comes Next?

Skills

★ extending an AAB pattern

★ using ordinal numbers

★ learning the names of the days of the week

You'll need

★ calendar markers

★ Calendar Numbers from Day 2

★ Days of the Week song

★ helper jar

It's a new day and time for another calendar marker. Ask children to join you in the Number Corner and call their attention to the calendar grid. Will the marker for today be a spider or a ladybug? What number will need to be glued on? In order to help children answer these questions, invite one of them to come up and point to the creatures on the October pattern strip. Read the pattern together. What parts of this pattern are on the calendar so far?

> **Children** *Mine's already up there. We have 2 ladybugs and a spider. We need a ladybug. No, we need a spider. Wait a minute! It goes ladybug, ladybug, spider—ladybug, ladybug, spider—I can show you. See. Here's what we have and here's the one we need. It's a ladybug!*

Day 3 Introducing the October Daily Routines (cont.)

Have a helper put the pattern piece on the grid. Do the children agree that it's correct? What numeral will you need to glue on it?

> **Children** *That's right. Ladybug, ladybug, spider, ladybug—tomorrow it has to be another ladybug. 1, 2, 3—it needs a 4.*

Once the proper numeral has been agreed upon, glue it to the new calendar marker. Then tell children that there's another way to read the numbers on the calendar. Model the use of ordinal numbers in naming each marker on the grid: first, second, third, fourth. Practice this together while a student helper points to the appropriate markers. Finally, sing the Days of the Week song together as another helper points to the names of the days at the top of the grid. (Once our children know the song, we sing only enough of it, starting with a Monday, to reach the current day. That way, they don't get so tired of it as the year goes on.)

This Month's Pattern Is

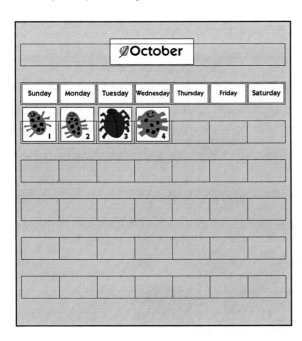

Our Month in School What's the Weather Like Today?

Skills

★ observing and describing weather conditions

★ recording observations in graph form

★ counting and comparing the graph data

You'll need

★ pocket chart

★ 3″ × 3″ construction paper squares in a single color (I for each child to use as a graphing card)

★ Weather cards (I of each)

Display the weather cards in your pocket chart and then take children outside to check the current conditions. Does it feel warm? Is the wind blowing

Day 3 Introducing the October Daily Routines (cont.)

hard? Is the sun shining? Are there lots of clouds, some covering the sun? Is it raining or snowing? Once they've decided how the weather seems to them, ask students to come to you and each get a graphing card. Then take everyone back inside and seat them in front of the pocket chart. Call a few at a time to place their graphing cards in the pocket beside the picture that seems to them to best characterize today's weather.

> **Teacher** *All right, weather reporters. What is the weather like today?*
>
> **Sammy** *I think it's really sunny out.*
>
> **Teacher** *Where should Sammy put his card to show that?*

Continue calling students up to post their cards until everyone has had a turn, and then ask them to tell you what they notice about the graph that has formed in the pocket chart.

> **Teacher** *Now that everyone has had a turn, what do you notice about the results of your weather reporting?*
>
> **Children** *Some people think it's all sunny, but they didn't look at the clouds. There was a cloud in front of the sun before the wind made it move. I think it's sunny and cloudy. It's not raining. Nobody chose that. Maybe some people chose wind because the clouds were moving. But it wasn't bad wind.*
>
> **Teacher** *So which weather card has the most cards by it? That's the one we'll post on the Our Month in School chart.*

Once children have determined which weather card was selected most frequently, have a helper place that card in the Our Month in School chart.

Day 3 Introducing the October Daily Routines (cont.)

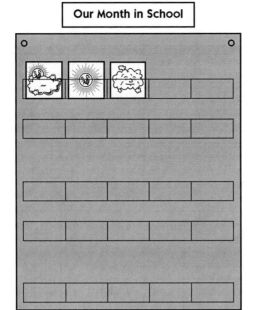

Sammy Most kids said it was cloudy, so that's the card we put up for today. I still think it should have been the sunny card.

. . . .

A Link Each School Day October

Skills

★ counting by 1's

★ counting by 10's

★ adding "1 more"

You'll need

★ 1″ × 7″ paper strips in the same colors you used for the September chain

★ glue

★ A Link Each School Day label

How many school days have passed so far this month? Help students determine how many paper loops they'll need and select helpers to quickly construct a paper chain of the proper length.

A Link Each School Day

Begin with the same color used at the end of September to make your first group of 10 in October. While the helpers are working, you might want to ask children to sing the Ladybird Beetle or the Spider song, if you introduced them yesterday.

Day 4

 CALENDAR COMPONENTS

Continuing Through October

The Daily Routines for October—the Calendar Grid, Our Month in School, A Link Each School Day, and Here's When We Were Born—have all been introduced and are hopefully going smoothly. As you move through the rest of the month, you might add a few new twists to these routines every now and then. We offer the suggestions below, but encourage you to be selective. You might decide some days to make the Calendar Grid the exclusive focus of your Number Corner instruction, and then take extra time for a discussion about the pattern, or have children practice writing the numerals in the day's date on individual chalkboards or white boards. Another day, you might decide to make the Our Month in School chart the focus, and repeat the class graphing activity from Day 3, or have children discuss the paper weather graph, as described below. Whatever you choose from day to day, be sure to keep your Number Corner sessions lively, varied, and short—an average of 10 minutes a day, three or four days a week.

. . . .

Note If there are days that you're not able to get to the Daily Routines at all, you might have a classroom helper update the Calendar Grid, Our Month in School, and A Link Each School Day, so you don't have to play catch-up with the whole class too often.

. . . .

. . . .

The Calendar Grid

Skills
★ extending an AAB pattern
★ looking for diagonal and vertical patterns
★ using cardinal and ordinal numbers
★ reading and writing numerals
★ learning the names of the days of the week

You'll need
★ the ladybug and spider markers
★ Ladybird Beetle song and Spider song
★ Days of the Week song
★ the rest of the Calendar Numbers from Day 3
★ individual chalkboards, chalk, and erasers *or* white boards and markers

Finding Patterns on the Grid
One of the things you can always do on the calendar grid is have children predict what the new calendar marker will be, using the pattern strip to help, as necessary. Have them figure out which calendar number needs to be

Day 4 Continuing Through October (cont.)

glued to the marker too. You can also encourage them to scan the entire grid for patterns—things that repeat in some way—particularly in the latter half of the month. As more and more markers are added, children may begin to notice diagonal patterns emerging. If you are using the AAB pattern shown, some students will be very excited to discover that the spiders in particular stand out in diagonal lines. Some may also begin to note the vertical patterns that show up on the grid.

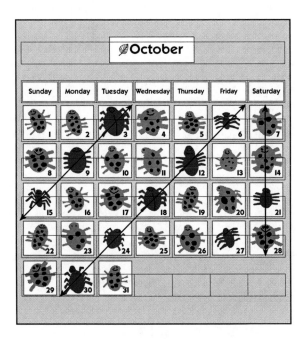

Counting and Reading Numerals
The Calendar Grid is a good place to practice counting, using both cardinal numbers (1, 2, 3...) and ordinal numbers (first, second, third), and you might have children count the markers once or twice a week. This helps to students who are still learning to count to 30. If you have a helper point to the markers as the class is counting, it also helps youngsters begin to read and recognize numbers between 1 and 30.

Reading the Day and Date
Begin modeling how to read the day and date:

Today is _____, October _____, _____.

Be sure to point to the day name, the month, the marker number, and the year label as you chant the date.

Writing Numerals
You might want to hand out chalkboards or white boards once or twice a week so children can practice writing the numerals from 1 through 5 or 6 through 10 as you go through the Daily Routines. As students begin to learn how to form

Day 4 Continuing Through October (cont.)

the numerals correctly, it's fun to write only the numbers that show up on the spiders, only the Monday numbers, only the Ladybugs' numbers, and so on. If you have many students who are still learning to read and write numbers to 10, you'll probably want to use only these numbers during these brief sessions.

Number Riddles

As students learn to read and write numerals with more ease, you might want to pose a number riddle once in awhile during Daily Routines. To do this, have children write the numbers 1 through 9 on their white boards. Then tell them that you have a slip of paper hidden in your pocket with one of these numbers on it. They can figure out what your mystery number is by making guesses and listening to the clues you give them.

Teacher *While you were busy practicing your numbers, I wrote one of them on a piece of paper and tucked it in my pocket. Can you guess which number?*

Children *Is it 8?*
No, it's 5 'cause we're 5!
5!

Teacher *No, it's not 5. My number is less than 5. What can you erase?*

Children *What does "less than 5" mean?*
She means it's not as big as 5. Take off 6 and 7.
We can take off 8 and 9 too. Get rid of 5! It's not as big as 5, remember? It has to be 3!

Teacher *Kari thinks it's 3, but my number is not on one of the spiders.*

Children *Take off 3 then.*
I know! It's 2!

Teacher *Good guess, but my number is bigger than 2.*

Suzy *It's 4! It has to be 4!*

Day 4 Continuing Through October (cont.)

Our Month in School Keeping Track of the Weather

Skills

★ observing and describing graph data

You'll need

★ Weather cards

★ What's the Weather Like Today? (Blackline NC 4, run 1 copy)

★ ¾" adhesive dots in several different colors (optional)

Continue adding a weather card to the Our Month in School chart each day. You may want to make weather observation a regular event when children first arrive in the morning or after a recess as they wait in line. Once you've gathered a couple of weeks of data, use the weather graph pictured below to examine and compare the various weather conditions that have occurred throughout the month so far. How many sunny days have there been so far? How many cloudy days? Has there been a day or two with lots of wind? Rain? Frost or snow? Color a box or affix an adhesive dot to the graph for each weather card posted on the Our Month in School chart. What do the children notice? How many different ways can they count the boxes that have been filled in above each weather picture?

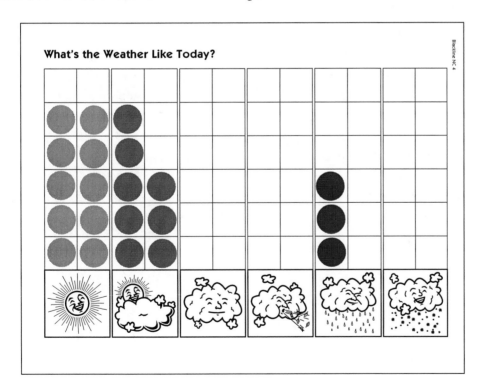

Note *If you teach in an area that would only have sunshine most days, combine two of these graphing sheets (removing the title on one) to provide enough spaces.*

Day 4 Continuing Through October (cont.)

. . . .

A Link Each School Day How Many Days Have We Been in School This Month?

Skills

★ counting by I's

★ counting by I0's

★ adding I more

You'll need

★ I" × 7" strips of construction paper in the same colors you used for September's chain

★ glue

How many school days have passed this month? Continue asking a helper to add a loop to the chain each day. When ten loops are in place, change colors and start the second group of ten. At the beginning of November, all the links you've collected for the first two months will be combined.

. . . .

Here's When We Were Born

Skills

★ naming the months of the year

You'll need

★ "Months of the Year" song (You'll find this song on the cassette tape or CD, *Songs for Number Corner by Greg and Steve*)

The last thing to consider when you do the Daily Routines this month is the Here's When We Were Born chart. Every so often, you might have the children look to see if anyone has a birthdate coming up in October or November. You might also begin reciting the names of the months to your children once in awhile, or possibly introduce the song, "Months of the Year." This little song takes a minute or two to sing, and simply sets the names of the months, along with another short verse, to a rather peaceful and lilting melody. When you sing this song with the children, you might point to each of the month labels on the Here's When We Were Born chart as the month is named.

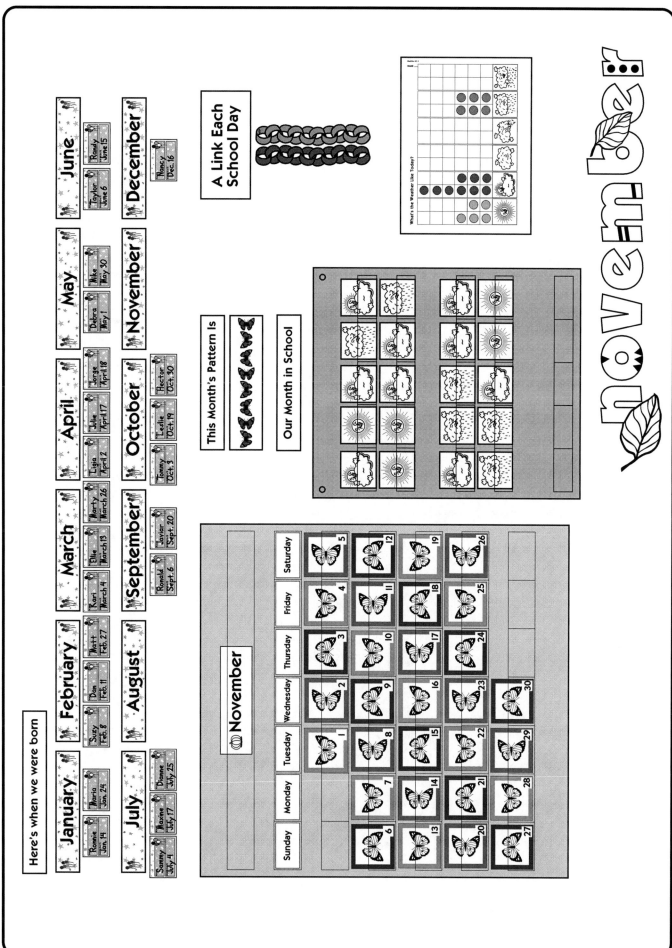

- -

Introduction

It's November and you may be headed into a busy time as parent confer-
ences, report cards, holidays, and perhaps changes in the weather loom large.
Meanwhile, things are probably starting to settle a bit in terms of your
children's comfort and familiarity with the whys and wherefores of kindergarten. You'll find that the Daily Routines this month are similar to October.
Students will work together the first day of the month to create new markers
for the calendar grid and to figure out how many days they've been in school
so far, but other than the addition of numeral writing practice associated with
the day's date, there are few changes. Just as in September and October,
you'll probably find that you'll need to devote the bulk of your math instruction to the Number Corner Daily Routines the first three or four days this
month. After that, these routines will compress to about 10 minutes a day
and may be done as part of your math instruction or daily opening. Once the
Daily Routines do smooth out, you'll want return to the Problems & Investigations lessons and Work Places in your *Bridges* Guide.

- -

*Note It will be important to leave the October calendar on display as Novem-
ber opens. Students will spend much of their math time the first day helping to
shift into the new month. We think their participation in this process is an
important part of feeling some ownership in the classroom. It both helps to
demystify school a bit and also provides some wonderful opportunities for
math instruction as you look back at the month that's just passed.*

- -

The Yearlong Paper Chain & A Link Each School Day

On the first school day of November, children will count the links they collected during October, help put the October paper chain together, and then add the October chain to the yearlong chain in order to determine how many days they've been in kindergarten so far. The second day, they'll start a new paper chain for November, to be added to the yearlong chain at the beginning of December.

The Calendar Grid

Before children create the new markers for the month, they'll review the pattern formed by the October calendar markers, count the markers to see how many days there were in October, and sing the Days of the Week song to determine the day on which the old month ended. Then they'll work together to create the new calendar markers for November while you clear the old ones off the grid. Although you may want to design your own markers, we've provided blackline drawings of butterflies for children to color and wash with watercolors.

In the three days that follow, students will begin to post their markers on the calendar grid, following the ABCABC pattern shown on the November pattern strip.

This Month's Pattern Is

Our Month in School

This month, children will continue to post a card to reflect the weather conditions each day they come to school. You'll also work with them again this month to show the data in the form of a bar graph.

Day 1

CALENDAR COMPONENTS

Introducing the November Daily Routines

Now that the first school day in November has arrived, the children help you shift the Number Corner display into the new month. Working with the completed October display, which you need to leave up for today's lesson, the students count the number of paper chain links they collected in October and then add them to the September chain to figure out how many days they've been in school altogether. Next, they count the number of markers on the calendar grid to determine how many days there were in the month of October and when the last day of that month occurred. Finally, they work to create new markers for the grid as you clear away the old ones.

· ·

Note *To support the current theme of the Bridges lessons—bugs—we've included blacklines for the children to use in making butterfly calendar markers. You'll also find a fact-filled piece about butterflies in the Poems & Songs Portfolio, which you might share sometime early in the month. If you have a favorite theme already planned for November, though, feel free to adapt the instructions on pages 79–81 so students can make calendar markers that better fit your plans.*

· ·

· ·

The Yearlong Paper Chain & A Link Each School Day

Skills

★ counting by 1's

★ counting by 10's and 1's

★ adding "1 more"

You'll need

★ September paper chain

★ October paper chain

★ 1" × 7" construction paper strips in the paper chain colors

★ scissors and glue

Open November's first Number Corner lesson by seating children close to your display. When everyone is settled, tell them that a new month has started. Explain that because November has arrived, you'll be working together to change some of the things on the calendar. The first thing you'll work on is the paper chain—taking down the links from October, adding them to the chain to find out how many days they've been coming to kindergarten so far this year, and starting a new chain for November.

Take a look at the paper chain links you collected during the month of October. How many links are there altogether?

Day 1 Introducing the November Daily Routines (cont.)

Once you've counted them one by one with the children, take a moment to explain that because the links have been organized in groups of 10, there's a faster way to count them. You may even have a few children who know that 10 and 10 are 20, and will be able to count on from there to determine the total. The rest will be perfectly happy to chant along as you point to the groups and count, "10, 20, 21, 22" (or whatever the number of links is you have on display), although they might not understand exactly what you're talking about.

Teacher Our October chain has 22 links. That means we spent 22 days in school during the month of October.

After you've counted the links both by 1's and by 10's and 1's, remove them from the calendar display. Have one of your students help you glue the 10's together. If you have any additional single links, don't include them yet.

Then connect the October chain to the September chain (make sure each group of 10 is an alternating color). If your September chain has additional links beyond the 10's, remove the extra(s) temporarily, making sure the children understand that you'll reattach them at the end of the entire chain.

When the chains are combined, ask to see if anyone can figure out how many links there will be altogether. (Though this is a big problem for most kindergartners, you might have a child or two who has already learned to count by 10's.) After giving students a minute to think about the problem, work with them to count the links by 1's. Then point out the groups of 10 formed by the alternating colors, and model counting by 10's.

Now, add the 1's to the end of the chain. (If you've had to cut any of these in taking apart the September chain, be sure to replace them with new links.)

Day I Introducing the November Daily Routines (cont.)

When the chain is complete, determine the total number of links by touching each link as the children count by 1's. Hang this chain somewhere else in the room— you'll need it again at the beginning of next month.

Finally, tell the children that you're going to start a new chain for November. How many school days have passed this month? Select a helper to construct a paper link for the new month, and attach it to the A Link Each School Day label.

As the helper is working, take a quick look at the Here's When We Were Born chart. Does anyone have a birthdate today? Does anyone have a birthdate coming up in November? How many children in class were born in November?

. . . .

The Calendar Grid Making the New Markers

Skills

★ reading a pattern

★ one-to-one correspondence

★ counting by I's to 3I

★ naming the days of the week

You'll need

★ Days of the Week song

★ completed October calendar grid

★ November calendar markers (Black-line NC 5, run I5 copies on white paper or cardstock and cut apart. You'll need 30 markers for the calendar. If you teach a double session, you'll want a marker for each child. You can use the extras as decorations.)

★ crayons

★ watercolor brushes, containers of water, and watercolors (optional)

★ a book with a photograph or drawing of a monarch butterfly

★ thirty 5″ squares of construction paper, 10 in each of 3 different colors to back the children's butterfly markers

It's time for the children to create a new set of markers for the calendar grid. Instead of cutting markers out of construction paper, they'll each color in one of the butterflies you've already run and do a watercolor wash over their coloring to simulate the sky (optional). Before tackling the task, though, take a few minutes to look back over the completed grid from October with your group.

Day I Introducing the November Daily Routines (cont.)

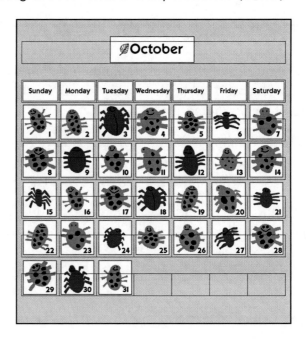

Read through the entire month's pattern as a helper points to each bug and everyone recites the sequence together. Then count the collection of bugs as a second helper points carefully to each number. When you reach 31, ask the children how many days there were in October. Although the answer will be quite obvious to some students, there are others who are still learning that the last number in a counting sequence also names the total (e.g., we counted to 31—therefore, there are 31 bugs on the grid, and there were 31 days in October). Next, sing the "Days of the Week" song as a third helper points to each of the bugs in turn, and then ask children what day of the week October ended on, and on what day of the week the new month will start.

Finally, explain to your students that you will clear away the old markers while they get the new ones ready. Show them the stack of the monarch butterfly markers you've prepared for them to color, and quickly show a colored photo or drawing so children will know this creature's colors.

Day 1 Introducing the November Daily Routines (cont.)

Then ask each youngster to color in one of the butterflies. (A few of your students will probably have to color in more than one unless you teach double session kindergarten. If you do have two groups, you might have everyone color in a marker and use the extras for room decorations.)

After they've colored in their butterflies, you might have children do a watercolor wash on their markers to give them a sky-like background. The easiest way we've found to do this is to have youngsters use watercolor brushes to paint their calendar markers with *water only* first, and then with colors from an ordinary tray of watercolor paints. Washing over the markers with water first will prevent children from painting over the colored butterflies so heavily that they're not visible. However, in case of disaster, if you catch the problem while the marker is still wet, use a paper towel to blot up the extra color. You may want to have everyone in class wash their markers with blue or turquoise to simulate sky, although pink, purple, orange, or yellow work too, to create the look of a sunrise or sunset. We do ask our children not to use black or brown.

Let children know that their markers will start going up tomorrow and that you have a very special pattern in mind. Like last month, you will number the markers as they are posted on the calendar grid each day.

. . . .

Note *You'll need to do a couple more things to prepare the calendar markers for tomorrow's lesson. Once they've dried thoroughly, you may want to outline each of the butterflies in black, using a permanent marker, to make them show up more clearly. This may be particularly important if a few of your students don't color very accurately yet. You'll also need to glue each of the butterflies to a 5" square of colored construction paper as shown in the following pattern:*

right-side up	sideways	upside-down	right-side up	sideways	upside-down
Color A backing	Color B backing	Color C backing	Color A backing	Color B backing	Color C backing

. . . .

Day 2

 CALENDAR COMPONENTS

Introducing the November Daily Routines

Today you introduce the pattern for the month (ABCABC), along with a poem about the monarch butterfly. Then you add a link to the paper chain for November and consider the total number of days you've spent in school. Finally, the children go outside to observe the weather and come back in to place their graphing cards beside the weather pictures they think best represent today's conditions. After everyone has voted, the appropriate weather card is posted in the Our Month in School pocket chart. November will be another month of watching, marking, and graphing the weather.

. . . .

The Calendar Grid

Skills

★ reading and extending an ABC pattern

★ learning facts about butterflies

This Month's Pattern Is

You'll need

★ November markers children made yesterday, prepared as described at the end of Day 1

★ November pattern strip (If you're using markers to support a different theme, you'll need to make a pattern strip to fit your markers.)

★ Calendar Numbers, sheets 1–2 (Blacklines NC 2–NC 3, run 1 copy on paper and cut apart)

★ The Monarch poem (Poems & Songs Portfolio A, pages PA.16–PA.19, create a wall chart or a big book with these pages)

Post the new pattern strip and ask children what they notice.

> **Children** *Those butterflies are all mixed up!*
> *They're flying everywhere.*
> *Some of them are going the wrong way.*
> *Sideways and up and down!*

> **Teacher** *You've noticed that even though they're all monarch butterflies, they're flying in different directions. Is there a pattern?*

> **Joshua** *It's up, then side, then down. It goes over and over that way!*

Day 2 Introducing the November Daily Routines (cont.)

Teacher *Do you agree with Joshua, boys and girls?*

Children *I think so.*
He's right!
They look kind of mixed up to me.

After a bit of discussion, point to each of the butterflies on the strip and read it together. You'll want to work with children to name each position accurately, but in words they all understand. The language might be as simple as, "up, sideways, down" or as complex as "right side up, sideways, upside down."

Then return to the calendar grid. Which direction will the first butterfly have to be flying and under what day of the week should it be posted? If no one in the group remembers, you might have to remind them of the day on which October ended (Tuesday, in this case). Point out that November must start on the day after the old month ended, and that you'll have to post two markers, one for yesterday and one for today, in order to bring the calendar grid up to date. According to the pattern strip, what direction will today's butterfly have to be flying? Once these questions have been settled and the markers posted, ask students what numeral should be placed on each. With the children's guidance, glue the calendar marker numbers on the first two markers.

If you have time before you move on, you might want to share the Monarch poem with your students. Read it to them once or twice. Then have them read it with you the third time around.

Day 2 Introducing the November Daily Routines (cont.)

The Monarch
by Donna Burk
illustrated by Tyson Smith

. . . .

A Link Each School Day How Many Days Have We Been in School This Month?

Skills
★ counting by 1's and by 10's and 1's

You'll need
★ the 1" × 7" paper strips
★ glue

Invite children to join you in the discussion area and draw their attention to the new paper chain for the month. How many school days have passed in November? Select a helper to construct a new paper link for today. While she's working, you might want to ask children to take a quick look at the Here's When We Were Born chart. Does anyone have a birthdate today, or one coming up soon?

Once today's link has been posted, ask children how many days they have been in kindergarten altogether. If time and interest permit, you might bring the year-long paper chain to the circle and count the links by 1's, including the two links posted so far for November. If time is short, model the process of counting all the links by 10's and 1's or hold off until another day to determine the ongoing total.

Day 2 Introducing the November Daily Routines (cont.)

Teacher 10, 20, 30, 40, 41, 42, 43—43 days in school, and 2 more if we count the new November links. That's 44, 45.

Our Month in School What's the Weather Like Today?

Skills

★ observing and recording weather conditions

★ making, reading, and interpreting a graph

You'll need

★ pocket chart

★ Weather cards

★ 3″ × 3″ construction paper squares (cut a class set)

★ Our Month in School chart with a Weather card for yesterday already posted

★ helper jar

Take a few minutes at the end of recess to observe and discuss the current weather conditions. As children come back into the classroom, have them join you in the discussion circle in front of the pocket chart. Post all six weather cards on the chart and then call on students a few at a time to post their graphing markers by the picture they think best portrays the day's weather.

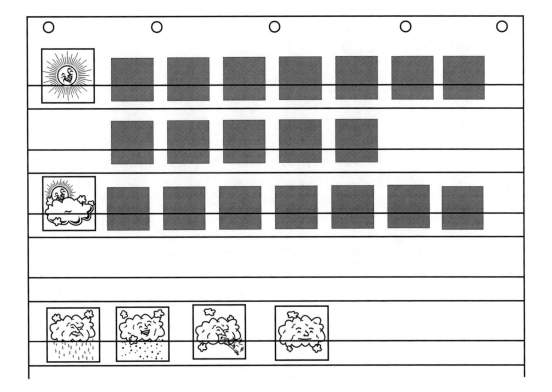

Day 2 Introducing the November Daily Routines (cont.)

What do students notice about the results? Encourage them to count the number of votes each weather card received and then compare the quantities. Which weather card got the most votes? Which got fewest? Were there any cards that weren't marked at all? How many more votes did one weather card receive than another?

> **Children** *The sun won! More people think it's sunny instead of sunny and cloudy. There's just a few clouds today, not lots, so sun is better.*
>
> **Teacher** *How many people thought that it was sunny today?*
>
> **Children** *1, 2, 3, 4, 5, 6, 7, 8, 9, 10, 11, 12! That's a lot.*
>
> **Teacher** *How many people thought it was partly cloudy today?*
>
> **Children** *7, I already counted. 1, 2, 3, 4, 5, 6, 7. Look, it's the same as these on this row by the sun.*
>
> **Teacher** *How many more children chose sunny than partly cloudy?*
>
> **Children** *12! What? Say that again. What do you mean?*
>
> **Teacher** *There are 12 graphing cards for sunny but only 7 cards for cloudy. How many more children chose sunny than cloudy?*
>
> **Mike** *Well, there are 7 and 7, but then sunshine has some more cards.*
>
> **Leslie** *Oh, maybe it's 5, because it's the same with the cards up there and here, but then these are the extras.*

Many young children find it very challenging to compare two or more quantities. Sometimes it's easier for them to figure how many more markers were placed beside one weather card than another on the basis of how many it would take for the card that received fewer to catch up with the card that received more. Another strategy that we've seen young children use to compare two quantities, or suggested ourselves, is to match the cards one to one and then count the cards that remain, the "extras." There will be many opportunities throughout the year to compare quantities, so don't feel that you have to get everyone to understand all of the concepts involved right now.

Once children have entered their votes and discussed the results, have a helper post the weather card for Day 2 on the Our Month in School chart.

Day 3

CALENDAR COMPONENTS

Introducing the November Daily Routines

Today have children post the next calendar marker and practice writing the numeral that matches today's date on their white boards or individual chalkboards, and attach another new link to the November paper chain. After recess, the children create another class graph to show which weather card best portrays today's conditions, and after examining the results, they post the chosen card in the Our Month in School chart.

. . . .

The Calendar Grid What Comes Next?

Skills

★ reading and extending an ABC pattern

★ naming the days of the week

You'll need

★ November pattern strip

★ calendar markers

★ Calendar Numbers from Day 2

★ helper jar

Invite children to join you in the discussion area and ask them to take a look at this month's pattern strip. Can they remember the names of the three butterfly positions in the pattern? Help students read the pattern by naming the position of each butterfly. If this pattern kept on going, what would come next? What two markers are already on the calendar grid? Ask children to identify today's butterfly position according to the pattern and post a marker from the collection that fits. Once the marker has been posted, work with children's guidance to glue on the correct numeral.

. . . .

Writing Today's Date

Skills

★ reading and writing numerals

★ forming numerals correctly

You'll need

★ white boards, markers, and erasers *or* chalkboards, chalk, and erasers placed in several locations around the room for easy pickup

★ Numeral Writing card for today's date

Day 3 Introducing the November Daily Routines (cont.)

Once the marker for today has been posted and numbered, have students collect writing materials and join you in the discussion area. (You might have them sit at their tables instead, if that works better in your classroom.) Post the Numeral Writing card that matches today's date and trace it with your fingers, demonstrating the correct stroke sequence as the children watch. Have them copy your motions in the air a couple of times and then with their fingers on the table or the carpet. Then ask them to practice writing the numeral on their boards.

If a few children are unable to get started, quickly write two or three copies of the numeral on their boards for them to trace over. The amount of time you can devote to activities like these will vary, but we feel that proper letter and numeral formation is important enough, even in kindergarten, to warrant some practice at least once a week. (We still have a few youngsters who do it "their way" no matter how solid our intentions and instruction are, however.)

. . . .

A Link Each School Day How Many Days Have We Been in School This Month?

Skills

★ counting

You'll need

★ the 1" × 7" paper strips (same colors as before)

★ glue

Yesterday there were two links on the paper chain for November. If you add one for today, how many will there be in all? As a helper works to add a link to the chain, you might ask the rest of your students to think about how many days they've been in kindergarten since the first day of school.

As you did yesterday, you might want to bring the yearlong paper chain into your discussion area and have students count all the links, including the

Day 3 Introducing the November Daily Routines (cont.)

three that have been posted so far in November, in order to answer this question. If time is short, however, skip this step today.

Teacher Here are all the links we collected in August/September and October. How many do you see?

Children Lots! It's a real lot. It's almost 100 days. I remember from yesterday—it's 43.

Teacher Let's count by 10's and 1's to check. 10, 20, 30, 40, 41, 42, 43.

Sarah But we have to add the 1's from over here. We have more than 43.

Teacher Oh, you're right. How many will we have if we add the 3 links we've collected so far in November to our yearlong chain?

Children Lots! 100! It's 3 more—that's 46. Let's count them all and see!

Our Month in School What's the Weather Like Today?

Skills
★ observing and recording weather conditions

★ making, reading, and interpreting a graph

You'll need
★ pocket chart

★ Weather cards

★ 3" × 3" construction paper squares to use as graphing markers (cut a class set)

★ Our Month in School chart

★ helper jar

Note If the weather conditions in your area are quite definite today—if, for instance, it's completely sunny, or pouring rain, or even snowing, and there really isn't any room for speculation or debate—you'll want to eliminate most of the steps outlined below and simply have a helper post the appropriate weather card in the Our Month in School chart.

As you did yesterday, take time at the end of recess to observe and discuss the current weather conditions. As children come back into the classroom, have them join you in the discussion circle in front of the pocket chart. Post all six weather cards on the chart and ask children to think about which of the cards best portrays the outdoor conditions. Then call on students a few at a time to post their graphing markers by the picture they believe best shows the day's weather.

Day 3 Introducing the November Daily Routines (cont.)

What do your students notice about today's results? Again, you'll want them to count and compare the numbers of cards from row to row.

Children *The sun and clouds won! More people think it's cloudy and sunny today. There are lots of clouds. Maybe it will rain.*

Teacher *How many people thought that it was partly sunny today?*

Children *1, 2, 3, 4, 5, 6, 7, 8, 9, 10, 11, 12, 13, 14! It's the same in both rows. 1, 2, 3, 4, 5, 6, 7 and 1, 2, 3, 4, 5, 6, 7.*

Teacher *How many people thought it was sunny today?*

Children *6, I could just tell because it wasn't as many as 7. It needed 1 more.*

Teacher *How many graphing cards are on our chart altogether?*

Children *1, 2, 3, 4, 5, 6, 7, 8, 9, 10, 11, 12, 13, 14, 15, 16, 17, 18, 19, 20! The sun would need a lot of cards to catch up.*

Using the helper jar, select one of the students to post the weather card for today on the Our Month in School chart.

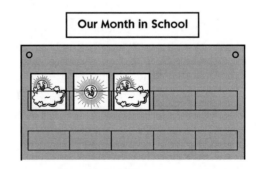

Day 4

CALENDAR COMPONENTS

Continuing Through November

The Daily Routines for November have all been introduced. Hopefully, these activities will be going smoothly enough in a day or two to return to the lessons in the *Bridges* Guide. We offer the following suggestions to help you keep the Number Corner routines lively and varied through the month. The key to keeping the sessions short—no longer than 10 minutes on any particular day—is to be very selective. You don't have to do each routine every day, and may choose to focus almost exclusively on the calendar grid one day, numeral writing practice another, and the growing paper chain or the weather cards a third. Another possibility is to keep what you do with each component brisk and run through all four in a single session.

. . . .

Note *If there are days that you're not able to get to the Daily Routines at all, you might have classroom helpers post the calendar markers and the weather cards, and add the new links to the paper chain, so you don't have to play catch-up with the whole class too often.*

. . . .

. . . .

The Calendar Grid

Skills
★ extending an ABC pattern

★ looking for diagonal and vertical patterns

★ using cardinal and ordinal numbers

★ reading numbers to 30

★ learning the names of the days

You'll need
★ November pattern strip

★ the Monarch poem

★ Days of the Week song

★ the rest of the markers for the month

★ the rest of the Calendar Numbers from Day 3

Finding Patterns on the Grid

One of the things you can always do on the calendar grid is have children predict what the new calendar marker will be, using the pattern strip to help. Have them figure out which calendar number needs to be glued to the marker too. You can also encourage students to scan the entire grid for patterns—things that repeat in some way—particularly in the latter half of the month. As more and more markers are added, children may begin to notice diagonal patterns emerging. If you are using the ABC pattern shown, some students will be very excited to discover that each of the butterfly positions

Day 4 Continuing Through November (cont.)

forms its own diagonal lines. Some may also begin to note the vertical patterns that show up on the grid.

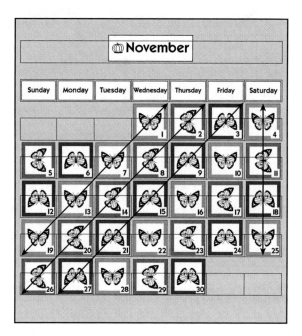

Counting and Reading Numerals

The calendar grid is a good place to practice counting, using both cardinal numbers and ordinal numbers, and you might have children count the markers once or twice a week. This can be a big help to students who are still learning to count orally to 30. If you have a helper point to the markers as the class is counting, it also helps youngsters begin to recognize numerals between 1 and 30 as well as to see the one-to-one correspondence required to count each new marker.

Reading the Day and Date

Continue to model how to read the day and date every so often:

Today is _____, November _____, _____.

Be sure to point to the day name, the date, the month, and the year as you chant the date.

. . . .

Writing Today's Date

Skills

★ reading and writing numerals to 9

★ reading and writing numbers between 10 and 30

You'll need

★ white boards, markers, and erasers, *or* chalkboards, chalk, and erasers

★ Numeral Writing cards

★ Numeral Writing Practice, 1's–10's (Blacklines NC 6–NC 15, optional)

Day 4 Continuing Through November (cont.)

You might want to hand out individual white boards or chalkboards once or twice a week so that every so often children can practice writing numerals as you go through the Daily Routines. Once you're past the 9th of the month, have children begin to practice writing 2-digit numbers by combining two of the numeral cards to form the date.

Teacher Today's the 14th, so we'll need both the 1 and the 4 card to help us practice writing the number 14.

As students begin to gain confidence, it's fun to write only the numbers that show up on the butterflies pointing up, only the Friday numbers, only the sideways butterflies, and so on.

. . . .

Note As an alternative to having students work on individual chalkboards or white boards, you might run copies of the Numeral Writing Practice sheets (Blacklines NC 6–NC 15) and use them occasionally. These pages may become especially useful a little later in the year as students gain fine-motor control and find it easier to complete paper-and-pencil tasks.

. . . .

Number Riddles

Continue to pose a number riddle once in awhile during Daily Routines. To do this, have children write the numbers 1 through 9 on their white boards. Then tell them that you have a slip of paper hidden in your pocket with one of these numbers on it. They can figure out what your mystery number is by making guesses and listening to the clues you give them.

> *Teacher While you were busy practicing your numbers, I wrote one of them on a piece of paper and tucked it in my pocket. Can you guess which number is hidden in my pocket?*
>
> *Ella Is it an up-butterfly number?*
>
> *Teacher What a great question! What are the upward-pointing butterflies' numbers so far?*

Day 4 Continuing Through November (cont.)

Children *1 and 4. 7 too!*

Teacher *You are just too clever, Ella. It is one of the up-butterfly numbers. Are there any numbers you can erase from your boards?*

Children *We can take away the 2. And erase the 3. Don't take away the 4. You can erase 5 and 6. Oh, we can do 8 and 9 too. This is going to be easy.*

Teacher *Let me choose a helper stick to guess my number. Randy.*

Randy *I think it's 7—it's the biggest.*

Teacher *Of these 3 numbers, 7 does mean the most, but my number is less than 7. What can you erase?*

Continue in this manner until children have figured out the mystery number.

. . . .

A Link Each School Day How Many Days Have We Been in School This Month?

Skills
★ counting by 1's
★ counting by 10's and 1's

You'll need
★ the 1″ × 7″ strips
★ glue

How many school days have passed this month? Continue asking a helper to add a loop to the chain each day. When ten loops are in place, change colors and start the second group of ten. How many school days have passed since the beginning of kindergarten? At the beginning of December, all the links you've collected in November will be added to the yearlong chain.

Day 4 Continuing Through November (cont.)

Our Month in School Keeping Track of the Weather

Skills
★ observing and describing weather conditions

★ making, reading, and interpreting a graph

You'll need
★ Weather cards

★ What's the Weather Like Today (Blackline NC 4, run I copy)

★ ¾" adhesive dots in several different colors (optional)

Continue adding a weather card to the Our Month in School chart each day. You may want to make weather observation a regular event when children first arrive in the morning or after a recess as they wait in line. Once you've collected two or three weeks of data, use the weather graph pictured below to examine and compare the various weather conditions that have occurred throughout the month so far. How many sunny days have there been? How many cloudy days? How many rainy days? High wind? Frost or snow? Color a box or affix an adhesive dot to the graph for each weather card posted on the Our Month in School chart. What do the children notice? How many different ways can they count the boxes that have been filled in above each weather picture?

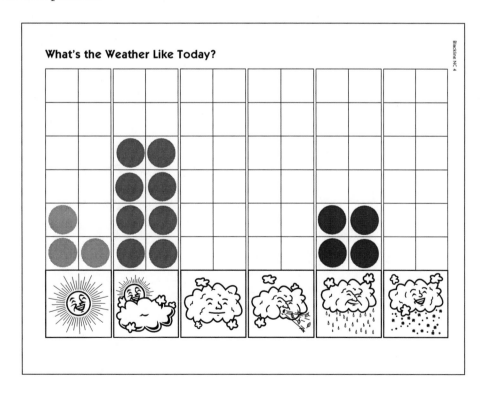

Children We've only had 3 days of sun. It's been cloudy a lot.

Day 4 Continuing Through November (cont.)

. . . .

Note *If you teach in an area that only has sunshine or rain most days, combine two of these graphing sheets (removing the title on one) to provide enough spaces.*

. . . .

. . . .

Here's When We Were Born

Skills

★ naming the months of the year

You'll need

★ "Months of the Year" song (You'll find this song on the cassette tape or CD, *Songs for Number Corner by Greg and Steve*)

The last thing to consider when you do the Daily Routines this month is the Here's When We Were Born chart. Every so often, you might have the children look to see if anyone has a birthdate coming up in November or December. You might also recite the names of the months to your children once in awhile, or sing the song, "Months of the Year," which you may have introduced last month. This little song takes a minute or two to sing, and simply sets the names of the months, along with another short verse, to a rather peaceful and lilting melody. On the occasions you sing this song with the children, point to each of the month labels on the Here's When We Were Born chart as the month is named.

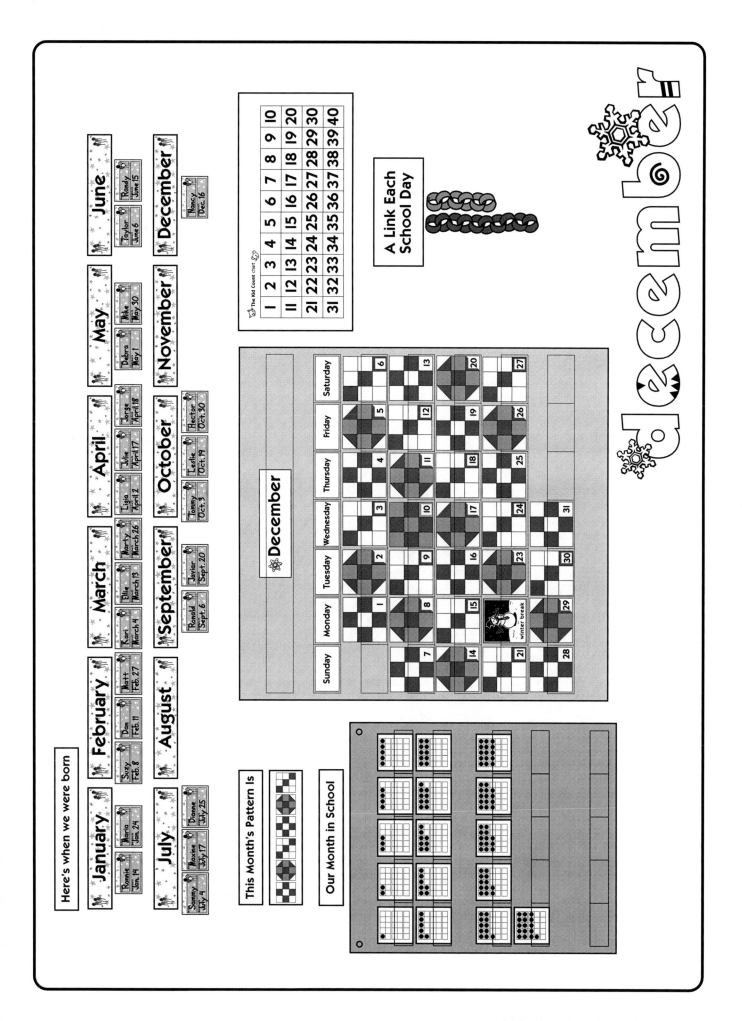

Here's when we were born

January
Ronnie Jan. 14
Maria Jan. 24

February
Suzy Feb. 8
Dan Feb. 11
Matt Feb. 27

March
Kurt March 4
Ellie March 13
Marty March 26

April
Ligia April 2
Julie April 17
Jorge April 18

May
Debra May 1
Mike May 30

June
Taylor June 6
Randy June 15

July
Sammy July 4
Maxine July 17
Dianne July 25

August

September
Ronald Sept. 6
Javier Sept. 20

October
Tommy Oct. 5
Leslie Oct. 19
Hector Oct. 30

November

December
Nancy Dec. 16

This Month's Pattern Is

Our Month in School

☃ December

Sunday	Monday	Tuesday	Wednesday	Thursday	Friday	Saturday
	1	2	3	4	5	6
7	8	9	10	11	12	13
14	15	16	17	18	19	20
21	winter break	23	24	25	26	27
28	29	30	31			

The Kid Count chart

1	2	3	4	5	6	7	8	9	10
11	12	13	14	15	16	17	18	19	20
21	22	23	24	25	26	27	28	29	30
31	32	33	34	35	36	37	38	39	40

A Link Each School Day

December

Introduction

It's December already—the months are flying by! This month's suggested calendar markers feature paper quilt blocks. They're fun to construct and provide a festive display. Along with the quilt markers, you'll find a new emphasis on numbers to 20 and beyond. The cards for the Our Month in School chart feature quantities of 20 or more, organized into frames of 10 for easier counting. In addition, there's a new counting routine that involves children in determining how many students are in class on any given day. The year-long paper chain continues to grow as the links that were collected in November are added and a new collection for December is begun.

Note Don't forget to leave the November calendar on display as December opens. Shifting the calendar display and learning the new routines will take most, if not all, your math time the first three days into December. After that, these routines will compress to about 10 minutes a day and may be done as part of your math instruction or daily opening. Once the Daily Routines smooth out, you'll want to return to the Problems & Investigations lessons and Work Places in your Bridges *Guide, or continue with another math program you may be teaching.*

The Calendar Grid

We think you and your children will love the new calendar markers, but because the process of making these patchwork creations is a little more complex than some of the markers, it will take a little longer. The first day, children will reexamine the November markers, reviewing the pattern and counting them one last time. They'll examine the pattern strip for December and choose which of the three quilt blocks they'll want to make. The second day, they'll construct the quilt blocks by gluing cut paper squares and triangles to blackline patterns.

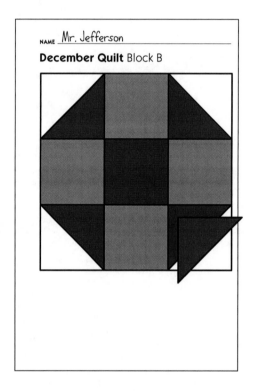

After the blocks are dry, trimmed, and labeled with children's names, they'll be added to the calendar grid in the ABC pattern set by the December pattern strip.

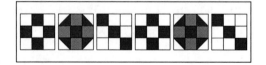

The Yearlong Paper Chain & A Link Each School Day

On the first school day of December, children will count the links they collected during November and then add them to the yearlong chain in order to determine how many days they've been in kindergarten so far. The second day, they'll start a new paper chain for December, to be added to the yearlong chain at the beginning of January.

Our Month in School

This month, children will post cards in the pocket chart that show a growing number of dots—one for each day they spend in school in December. The dots on these cards have been arranged on special grids known as ten-frames, which allow students to discover relationships between quantities visually. On the card below, which would be posted on the 8th school day of the month, some students may notice that 8 is 3 more than 5, and 2 less than 10.

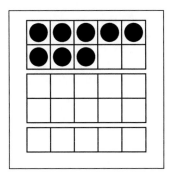

As you use these cards through the next several months, 5 and 10 will gradually come to have a special place in children's thinking and, over time, many students will also begin to recognize quantities between 0 and 5 instantly. Some may begin to think of numbers such as 8 in terms of smaller groups—2 and 2 make 4, and another set of 2 and 2 make 8 in all. At the same time, ten-frames accommodate children who are still learning to count quantities one by one. We have found the ten-frames to be one of the more powerful ways to help kindergartners begin to understand numbers to 10, 20, and even 30, and we use this visual model throughout the rest of the *Bridges* program as well as in the Number Corner.

The Kid Count

This new routine gives children another, and very compelling, reason to count and read numbers to 20 and beyond—that of taking attendance. In the Kid Count, children learn to count off around the circle to find out how many students are in class on any given day. They also use a new counting chart to help determine how many children, if any, are absent.

🐱 The Kid Count chart 🐭

1	2	3	4	5	6	7	8	9	10
11	12	13	14	15	16	17	18	19	(20)
21	22	23	24	(25)	26	27	28	29	30
31	32	33	34	35	36	37	38	39	40

Teacher *How far is it from 20 to 25?*

Julie *5! Just the 20 and 5 more.*

Mike *I can show on my fingers.* (He holds up 5 fingers outstretched.)

Teacher *Julie and Mike are pretty convinced that it's 5. Let's try counting it on the chart. I'll use my pointer and we'll start at 20.*

Children and Teacher *20—21, 22, 23, 24, 25.*
Lots!
It's 5—I did it on my fingers like Mike.

Teacher *You're right. There are 5 kids missing. Let's look at our class list and see if we can figure out who's absent.*

In a variation of the Kid Count, also introduced this month, each child in class is given a number card. These are distributed in random order, and after giving students a minute to help each other determine how many dots they have on their cards, the teacher asks children to line themselves up in order.

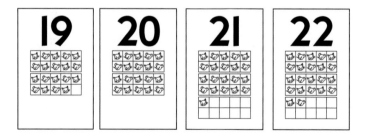

The number cards for this activity use the same ten-frame format as the cards on the Our Month in School chart, providing youngsters with yet another opportunity to encounter quantities that have been organized with reference to groups of 5 and 10.

Day I

 CALENDAR COMPONENTS

Introducing the December Daily Routines

After some closing work with the November calendar, your class will begin the shift into December today. First they count the number of paper chain links they collected in November and add them to the yearlong chain to figure out how many days they've been in school so far. They count the number of markers on the calendar grid to determine how many days there were in the month of November and when the last day of the month occurred. During this part of the lesson, remove the butterflies from the grid, clearing the way for the new markers. Finally, show children the new pattern for the calendar grid, which involves three different quilt blocks. After taking a careful look at all three, each student chooses which block he or she wants to make tomorrow.

. . . .

Note *If you have a favorite theme already planned for December feel free to adapt the Calendar Grid instructions today and tomorrow so students can make calendar markers that better fit your plans. Be sure to make a pattern strip for the month to match your markers.*

. . . .

. . . .

The Yearlong Paper Chain & A Link Each School Day

Skills

★ counting by I's

★ counting by 10's and I's

You'll need

★ yearlong paper chain

★ November paper chain

★ I" × 7" construction paper strips (continue to use the same 2 colors)

★ scissors and glue

Open December's first Number Corner lesson by seating children close to your display. When everyone is settled, tell them that a new month has started. Explain that because December has arrived, you'll be working together to change some of the things on the calendar. The first thing you'll work on is the paper chain—taking down the links from November and adding them to the yearlong chain. You'll also start a new chain for the month of December.

Take a look at the paper chain links you collected during the month of November. How many 10's are displayed? Are there any additional 1's? How many links are there in all for the month of November? Count them one by

Day I Introducing the December Daily Routines (cont.)

one with the children. Then model counting the collection by 10's and 1's and remove them from the calendar display. If you have 2 groups of 10 links, cut open the link at the end of one of them and connect the 2 groups. If you have any additional links, don't attach them yet. (In the case shown here, there were only 19 days of school in the month.)

Teacher *Our November chain has 1 group of 10 and 9 extra 1's—you counted 19 in all. How many more links would this group of 9 need to be a full 10?*

Children *9—10*
10 is next after 9.
Just 1 more link.
We didn't get enough.

Before you add the November links to the yearlong chain, remove the 1's from the end temporarily so you can combine the groups of 10 first. If, as is the case in the situation pictured below, you can combine some of the extra 1's to create a new 10, do so. This will mean switching the color of at least one of the links, and may be something you want to do fairly quickly, without trying to explain it in any great detail at this time.

Teacher *There are 43 links in our yearlong chain and 19 to add from November. Let's remove the last 3 links from the yearlong chain so we can combine all the 10's.*

Teacher *This is interesting. Does anyone see a way we can make another group of 10 here?*

Kari *Take one of the 1's from the 3 and move it to the 9?*

Teacher *Okay—we'll have to switch colors to make it work, and then we'll have another group of 10. Wow! Our chain is really going to be long when we get the whole thing put together.*

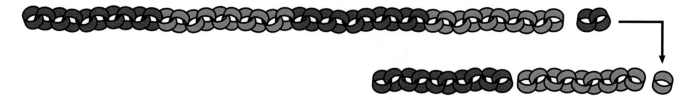

Day 1 Introducing the December Daily Routines (cont.)

When all of the possible 10's have been combined, have a student help you stretch the chain out on the floor. Can anyone figure out how many links there are altogether? (Though this is a big problem for most kindergartners, you might have a child or two who has already learned to count by 10's.) After giving students a minute to think about the problem, point out the groups of 10 formed by the alternating colors. As you point to the color groups, count them by 10's, and repeat the sequence as the children join in. Then ask them to go through the counting sequence a third time with their hands outstretched to show 10 fingers for each number. (These finger motions provide a tactile experience each time the children name one of the numbers in the counting-by-10's sequence. This will help some youngsters remember the sequence—10, 20, 30, 40, and so on—more readily.)

Then, add the 1's to the end of the chain. When the chain is complete, count the links one more time, touching each as the children count by 1's.

> **Teacher** *62 days in all—wow! We have been in school a long time!*

Finally, tell the children that you're going to start a new paper chain for December. How many school days have passed this month? Select a helper to quickly construct a paper link for the new month, and attach it to the A Link Each School Day label.

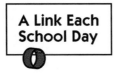

As the helper is working, take a quick look at the Here's When We Were Born chart. Was anyone born today? Does anyone have a birthdate coming up in December? How many children in class were born in December?

Day 1 Introducing the December Daily Routines (cont.)

. . . .

The Calendar Grid One Last Look at November

Skills

★ reading an ABC pattern

★ counting by 1's to 30

★ naming the days of the week

You'll need

★ Days of the Week song

★ completed November calendar grid

★ a 5″ × 5″ piece of construction paper in a bright color

Before you dismantle November's calendar grid, have the children read through the entire month's butterfly pattern as a helper points to each marker. Then as a second helper points to the markers again, have students recite each of the counting numbers. Finally, sing the Days of the Week song for the entire month, quickly removing each of the markers from the grid as the days are named. When you get to the last marker, stop singing. What day *was* that? Then slip a brightly colored square of construction paper into the pocket in the top row of the now-empty grid under the very next day to help everyone remember the starting point for posting the new markers, once they're made.

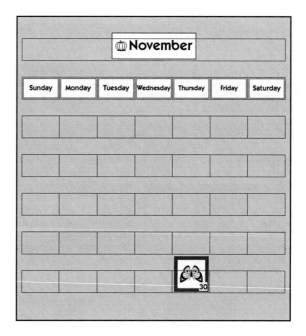

Teacher *Which day was the last day of November?*

Children *Thursday!*

Teacher *So the new month will start on…*

Children *Friday!*
It has to be Friday—that's what comes next in the song.

Day I Introducing the December Daily Routines (cont.)

Teacher *We won't have enough room for our new markers on this grid if we have to start way at the bottom, so we'll have to go back up to the top row and find the pocket that comes under Friday there. Does anyone see the word "Friday" along the top of the grid?*

Children *It's the one with F.*
That's it! It has to be—it's the only one that starts with F.

Teacher *You're right, and I'm going to mark this pocket with a big square of red paper to help us remember where to start our new markers when we get them made.*

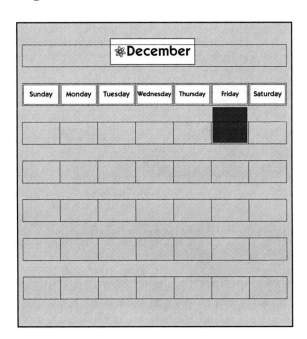

The Calendar Grid Which Marker Do You Want to Make?

Skills

★ exploring an ABC pattern

★ observing squares and triangles and how they fit together

. . . .

Note On the December pattern strip, we use a red, white, and blue color scheme. Pick colors that you and your children like. If you want to spend a bit of money, it's striking to use gift wrap (with a small calico-type print) as one of the color choices, but it does take more time to cut the squares on the paper cutter.

. . . .

You'll need

★ December pattern strip

★ a sample of each of the December Calendar quilt blocks (Blacklines NC 16–NC 18, make one of each block in the same colors the children will use. See page 114 for instructions.)

★ pocket chart

★ a 3″ × 5″ card for each student with his or her first name written on it

★ helper jar (You'll need each student's stick for this activity.)

Day 1 Introducing the December Daily Routines (cont.)

Now that all the old markers have been cleared away, it's time to get started making new ones. After getting children up for a brief stretch and wiggle, gather them back to the Number Corner, and explain that you're going to show them the new pattern strip for the month. If they take a close look at it, they'll be able to see what the new markers look like, and how they'll be patterned.

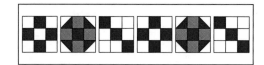

Teacher *Since the weather has cooled off and winter officially begins this month, I thought it would be a good idea to have our December calendar grid look like a quilt. On the chilly days, we can think about how cozy it would feel to wrap up in a beautiful warm quilt. Here's our new pattern strip. What do you notice about these quilt blocks?*

Children *Those are beautiful.*
They all have squares but one has triangles too.
I like the one that looks like a soccer ball.
The first one is like Tic Tac Toe.
If you count 1, 2, 3, (the third block) that one has only 3 blue squares.
It has 6 red squares.
The first one and the third one have 9 squares.
The soccer ball has 5 squares and some triangles too.

After students have had a chance to share their observations, explain that tomorrow, they'll each be making a quilt block like one of the blocks on the pattern strip. Show them the blocks you've already made so children can see how they look in "real life," and then post the three along the top row of your pocket chart. Tell students that since this is an ABC pattern, they'll need to make an equal number of each kind of block; you'll need roughly a third of them to choose each design. Hand out their name cards and then as you pull sticks out of your helper jar, have each of them post his or her name card under the quilt block he or she wants to make tomorrow. It will undoubtedly require a bit of negotiation and compromise to get children to sign up for the blocks in equal numbers. (If you have two sessions, it won't really matter—you'll have extra blocks to decorate the room. If you have one group, a few children will have to make extra blocks anyway. It's interesting, though, to see how the children respond to the challenge of creating three roughly equal groups by choice. Handling things this way also offers a great opportunity to count and compare quantities as students place their name cards on the chart.)

Teacher *Nancy, yours in the very last stick out of the jar. Which block do you want to make tomorrow?*

Day 1 Introducing the December Daily Routines (cont.)

Nancy *I want to make the one in the middle, but there's no place for me to put my name.*

Teacher *There's one more pocket at the bottom of the chart. I'm not sure I understand what you mean.*

Kari *She's the last one. All the quilts have the same number—7, 7, and 7. There's no place for her.*

Teacher *Oh, I see. All 3 groups are equal, and if Nancy puts her card in, there will be 1 extra of one of the blocks. Hmm—what shall we do about that?*

Leslie *I could make another one, and Maria could too. Then we'd have 8 and 8 and 8.*

Teacher *That's a great idea. We're going to need 31 blocks altogether so we'll need several of you to make an extra block tomorrow, but we can wait to decide who should do that.*

Day 2

 CALENDAR COMPONENTS

Introducing the December Daily Routines

Today's session begins with the introduction of a new routine, the Kid Count. It's quick, fun, and designed to provide plenty of practice this month and next in counting, reading, and beginning to understand numbers to 20 or more. Next, have children add a new link to December's paper chain. Then introduce a new set of cards for the Our Month in School chart, designed, like the Kid Count, to help children become more familiar with the numbers to 20. Finally, set students to work making the new quilt block markers for December's calendar grid.

· ·

The Kid Count

Skills

★ counting by 1's

★ using 1-to-1 correspondence

★ reading numbers to 20 and beyond

The Kid Count chart

1	2	3	4	5	6	7	8	9	10
11	12	13	14	15	16	17	18	19	20
21	22	23	24	25	26	27	28	29	30
31	32	33	34	35	36	37	38	39	40

You'll need

★ a short pointer of some kind (This could be something as simple as a ruler or as enchanting as a length of wooden dowel painted and glittered to resemble a magic wand. A hand puppet would also work well.)

★ The Kid Count chart (post this in your Number Corner today)

★ an overhead marking pen in a bright color (orange or red; not black)

Open today's lesson by asking students to sit in a circle. Explain that because it's a new month, you're going to introduce a brand new Number Corner activity. This one is called the Kid Count, and you'll use it to find out how many children are in class today.

> **Teacher** *Boys and girls, we're going to count everyone to find out how many children are in class today. The first time we do it, I'll stand behind each one of you and we'll count together every time I point to a new child.*

Help the children count the number of youngsters in class as you walk around the outside of the circle, pointing to each youngster in turn. You might want to hold something in your hand to focus everyone's attention as you point. As mentioned above, this could be something as simple as a ruler.

Day 2 Introducing the December Daily Routines (cont.)

If you want to lend a touch of sheer magic, though, use a seasonal pointer of some sort, a "magic wand," or even a hand puppet. Then ask the children to count around the circle again, but this time as you walk and point, have each youngster clap and say the number when it's his or her turn. If someone isn't able to say the number, everyone should help.

> **Teacher** *25! That's wonderful! I'm so glad you're all here. Let's count again. This time, when it's your turn, clap and at the same time say your counting number. If you don't know what number comes next, just clap and then everyone can help you.*

Then gather children into your Number Corner area and draw their attention to the Kid Count chart. Can anyone find the number that shows how many children there are in class today?

> **Teacher** *Let's look at our new counting chart. Can anyone find the number that tells how many children are in class today?*

> **Children** *25—where's 25?*
> *It has a 5 in it, I know, 'cause it's twenty-five.*
> *It's a 2 and then a 5—my mommy told me.*
> *I'll show you!*

Once the number has been located on the chart, circle it with your brightly-colored overhead marker. Then, using your pointer (ruler, magic wand, hand puppet), point to each number on the chart as the children count with you one more time, starting from 1.

Day 2 Introducing the December Daily Routines (cont.)

```
The Kid Count chart

 1   2   3   4   5   6   7   8   9  10
11  12  13  14  15  16  17  18  19  20
21  22  23  24 (25) 26  27  28  29  30
31  32  33  34  35  36  37  38  39  40
```

Children *1, 2, 3, 4, 5, 6…25.*
That one says 25.

Teacher *You're right, and we have 25 children here in class today.*
Great counting!

. . . .

A Link Each School Day How Many Days Have We Been in School This Month?

Skills

★ counting by 1's

★ counting by 10's

★ adding "1 more"

You'll need

★ the 1″ × 7″ paper strips

★ glue

Once the Kid Count has been made, direct children's attention to a second counting task. How many school days have passed in December so far? Select a helper to construct a new paper link for today.

While she's working, you might want to ask children to take a quick look at the Here's When We Were Born chart. Does anyone have a birthdate today, or one coming up soon?

Day 2 Introducing the December Daily Routines (cont.)

. . . .

Our Month in School Introduce the Ten-Frame Dot Cards

Skills
★ counting by I's

★ instant recognition of quantities to 5

★ recognizing "I more"

★ seeing quantities in relationship to 5
   and to I0

You'll need
★ Ten-Frame Dot cards

★ helper jar

If it's the second school day in December, there are two links now hanging in the Number Corner. The new cards for the Our Month in School chart will give children a different way to look at this quantity by showing how it looks organized onto a ten-frame. These frames will be familiar to your students by now if you're using the full *Bridges* program. If not, they will become quite familiar over the next two months. Ask helpers to post the first two cards in the Our Month in School chart and then ask children to share any observations they may have. Discuss the new cards briefly and then move along.

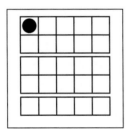 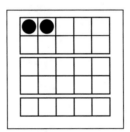

Children *It goes 1, 2!*
There's 1 spot, and then 2.
It's just like counting—I bet 3 comes tomorrow.
We have 2 circles in the paper chain and 2 spots on that card.
It's a new dot for each day.

Teacher *Most of you seem to think that these cards will show a new dot for each day we're in school this month. How will you know if you're right about that?*

Suzy *We just have to wait 'til tomorrow to see if it's 3 dots on the card.*

Teacher *Then you'll know for sure?*

Suzy *For sure!*

Day 2 Introducing the December Daily Routines (cont.)

. . . .

The Calendar Grid Making the New Markers

Skills

★ exploring triangles and squares

★ counting

★ rotating and matching shapes

. . . .

Note In the December Pattern Strip and the lesson as written here, we've used white for Color A, red for Color B, and blue for Color C. Cut three 12″ × 18″ sheets of paper cut into 1½″ squares for each of the first two colors, A and B. Also, cut one sheet of 12″ × 18″ paper in Color C into 1½″ squares, and cut one sheet of 9″ × 12″ paper into triangles for each of the two colors, A and B. This will give you enough for a class of 30. It's striking to use gift wrap (with a small overall calico-type print) for Color A or Color B.

. . . .

You'll need

★ I sample of each of the December Calendar quilt blocks posted in the pocket chart, along with children's name cards from yesterday

★ December Quilt Block A–Block C (Blacklines NC 16–NC 18, depending on the size of your group(s) run 5–10 copies of each sheet plus a few extra. Cut the sheets in half so each child receives I block to work with.)

★ 1½″ × 1½″ squares of construction paper in colors A, B, and C

★ right triangles cut from 1½″ squares of construction paper in colors A and B

★ glue

★ Calendar Numbers sheets I–2 (Blacklines NC 2–NC 3, make I copy of each and cut apart)

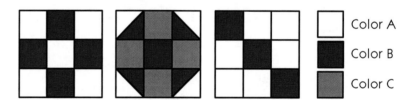

Color A
Color B
Color C

After a brief stretch & wiggle break, explain that the last thing you're going to do today is make the new calendar markers. Draw their attention to the premade quilt blocks and the name cards in the pocket chart from yesterday and give them a moment to remember which of the three blocks they chose.

> **Children** *I'm doing the soccer ball one in the middle.*
> *I got that Tic Tac Toe one—it's my best.*
> *I wanted the soccer ball, but it was all full, so I picked the one on the end with all those red squares. It looks kind of like a double arrow.*

After children have had a chance to discuss yesterday's choices, display a blackline copy of each of the quilt block patterns. Show students how they'll be gluing construction paper squares and triangles directly on top of the same shapes on the blackline pattern sheets. Then explain that in order to make these calendar markers, everyone will need to use the same secret code for the colors—red to cover the dark gray regions, blue to cover the light

Day 2 Introducing the December Daily Routines (cont.)

gray regions, and white wherever they see white. Tell them if they're not sure which color to put where, they can look at your examples in the pocket chart.

Explain that it is *very important* to make each shape fit perfectly inside the lines of the same shape on the blackline pattern. Dot some glue on the back of one of the red paper triangles and then ask a student to come up and place the triangle exactly over a dark gray triangle on the first pattern sheet.

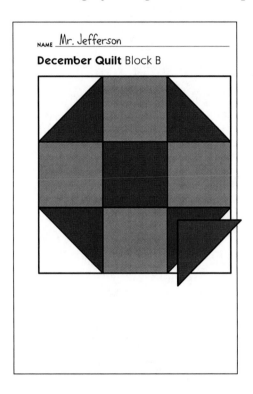

NAME Mr. Jefferson

December Quilt Block B

Ella This is kind of hard.

Joshua Just turn it a little bit and it'll fit right in there. Want me to help you?

Choose another helper or two to add more red paper shapes—three more triangles and a single square—to the sheet in order to cover all the dark gray shapes. Are children getting the idea that they'll need lots of patience to get their shapes in the proper spaces? Do they understand that once they've glued down squares and triangles to cover the dark gray shapes on their sheet, they'll need to switch to blue to cover the light gray portions on their pattern sheets, and then to white to cover the triangles (in the example above)?

After your demonstration, distribute the paper quilt blocks the children chose yesterday and send them out to work. You'll need to circulate throughout this process to be certain they have the idea. Encourage them to help one another get the colored construction paper shapes properly placed and aligned, and remind them to put their names on their papers when they're finished.

Day 2 Introducing the December Daily Routines (cont.)

. . . .

Note *To prepare the markers for use on the calendar grid tomorrow, write each child's name on his or her finished block, and trim away the margins using a paper cutter (much faster than scissors). Arrange the blocks in order according to the pattern strip. Use a sheet of the Calendar Numbers (Blacklines NC 2–NC 3) to glue the appropriate number to each block.*

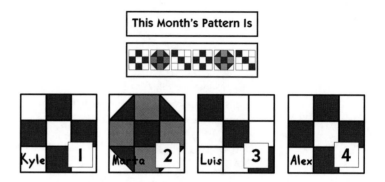

You'll need to interrupt the patterned sequence of quilt blocks with the Winter Break Calendar marker. Insert the Winter Break card on the date of your last school day before vacation. While you won't need all the markers this month, you'll be using them at the beginning of January, when you'll post all the markers for the month of December. (If you want to reuse the Winter Break Card in future years, attach the calendar number with tape instead of glue.)

. . . .

Teacher *Wow! Last day of school is the 22nd. I hadn't realized how late we're getting out this for our winter break.*

After they're prepared, store the entire set of markers by the calendar grid in a way that keeps the blocks hidden so the children have an opportunity to figure out what quilt block and what number comes next in the pattern each day.

Day 3

CALENDAR COMPONENTS

Introducing the December Daily Routines

Work with the children today to post as many of the new markers as necessary. Do the Kid Count again to determine how many children are in class today. If the total differs from yesterday's, students determine the difference, using the new Counting Chart. Finally, the children extend the paper chain by one link and add a new card to the Our Month in School chart.

. . . .

The Calendar Grid Getting Started

Skills

★ reading and extending an ABC pattern

★ counting and reading numerals

You'll need

★ December markers children made yesterday, prepared as described at the end of Day 2

★ December pattern strip

Draw children's attention to the Calendar Grid. It's the third school day in December, but quite possibly a weekend has gone by too, so you may have more than three markers to put up today. Start by examining the position of the colored square you used to mark the first day of the month when you removed the November markers from the grid. What day was that? What day is it now? Work with the children to figure out how many days have passed since the first of the month, and how many markers need to be posted today.

> **Teacher** *I trimmed your quilt blocks yesterday after school and they're all set to go. Now all we have to do is figure out where to put them! When the month first started and we removed all the November markers from our calendar grid, we put up a square of red paper to help us remember where to start the new month. How about singing the Days of the Week Song with me to find out which day this square is on? I'll point—you sing, okay?*

> **Children** *Monday, Tuesday, Wednesday, Thursday—Friday!*
> *I knew that!*
> *I remembered it was Friday.*
> *Just read the F on that word—it's the only one that starts with F.*

> **Teacher** *Good work! But you know what? Some days have passed since then, and it's already Tuesday, which is right here on the grid. How many markers are we going to need for all the days that have passed so far?*

Day 3 Introducing the December Daily Routines (cont.)

Children *1, 2, 3, 4—4 markers.*
No, 5, 'cause we need 1 for today, don't forget.

After the children have discussed the problem, work with them to post the markers in the correct pattern on the grid. To do this, they'll need to refer to the pattern strip. They'll probably have an easier time discussing their predictions if they're able to come up with names for each of the three quilt blocks. In the dialogue below, you'll notice that the group has christened each block with a name that captures something about the picture formed by the squares and triangles.

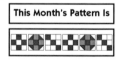

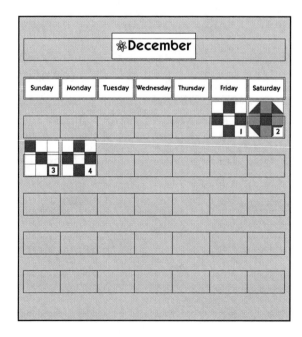

Teacher *Wow! You have done a great job of figuring out the first 4 markers for the month, and they look absolutely beautiful up here. What kind of quilt block will we need for today, and what number will it be?*

Day 3 Introducing the December Daily Routines (cont.)

Children *The soccer ball!*
It goes Tic Tac Toe, soccer ball, steps—Tic Tac Toe, soccer ball, then steps.
It has to be the soccer ball with a 5 on it.
The 5 ball!

Teacher *What makes you so sure?*

Maria *It's a pattern!*

Dianna *It's what has to come next. The soccer ball always comes next after the Tic Tac Toe, and it goes 1, 2, 3, 4, 5.*

. . . .

The Kid Count

Skills

★ counting by 1's

★ using 1-to-1 correspondence

★ reading numbers to 20 and beyond

★ exploring the idea of finding the difference

You'll need

★ the Kid Count chart with the number still circled from yesterday

★ overhead marking pen

★ short pointer or hand puppet

Once the calendar markers have been posted, have children stretch, wiggle, and return to sitting in a circle. Tell them that you're going to do the Kid Count again to find out if everyone's in class today. Do they remember how many children they counted around the circle yesterday? Will it be the same number today? If you listen carefully to students' responses to these questions, you may make some interesting discoveries. Some children will remember the total from yesterday easily, or even refer back to the counting chart, explaining that the number is right there, circled in red. Others may not remember at all. Some students may tell you that the number of children today will be different because an absent student has returned, or because someone is missing. Others may believe the number will be different because they lack the skills to carry numbers from one experience to the next.

After a bit of speculation, start the count. Begin with the child closest to you and have her clap and say "one." Continue around the circle until each child has had a turn to clap and say the next number in the sequence. (You and the other students can help when someone doesn't know his or her number yet.)

Teacher *Boys and girls, we're going to count 1 by 1 again today to find out if everyone is here. Do you remember how you clapped and counted when it was your turn yesterday? Let's get started.*

Day 3 Introducing the December Daily Routines (cont.)

Teacher *20! That's not enough. Let's count again to be sure we did it right. It is supposed to be 25.*

Ask the children to count again to be sure the total is correct, especially if it's different from yesterday's total.

Children *20! It's just the same. We were right! Maybe lots of kids have colds.*
I'm sick too, but my mommy made me come to school.

Teacher *Let's look at the counting chart. Maybe we can use it to figure out how many children are missing. Our total from yesterday is circled. Does anyone remember what this number says?*

🐱 **The Kid Count** chart 🐭

1	2	3	4	5	6	7	8	9	10
11	12	13	14	15	16	17	18	19	(20)
21	22	23	24	(25)	26	27	28	29	30
31	32	33	34	35	36	37	38	39	40

Julie *It's 25. I think 5 kids are gone today, 'cause it's 20 and then 5.*

Tommy *It's a lot. Leslie's gone and so is David.*

Teacher *This is an interesting problem all right. Julie's pretty sure 5 kids are absent, and Tommy can already think of 2 friends he doesn't see.*

Day 3 Introducing the December Daily Routines (cont.)

> *Kari* *Maxine's gone too.*
>
> *Maxine* *No, I'm not! I'm right here!*

If today's total differs from yesterday's some children will be fascinated to find the difference in the two numbers, while others will be far more interested in determining who's missing. You'll probably want to deal with the second concern by using your class list, but the first can be addressed by circling today's number on the counting chart, and then working with children to determine the difference between yesterday's and today's totals.

> *Teacher* *How far is it from 20 to 25?*
>
> *Julie* *5! Just the 20 and 5 more.*
>
> *Mike* *I can show on my fingers.* (He holds up 5 fingers outstretched.)
>
> *Teacher* *Julie and Mike are pretty convinced that it's 5. Let's try counting it on the chart. I'll use my pointer and we'll start at 20.*
>
> *Children and Teacher* *20—21, 22, 23, 24, 25.*
> *Lots!*
> *It's 5—I did it on my fingers like Mike.*
>
> *Teacher* *You're right. There are 5 kids missing. Let's look at our class list and see if we can figure out who's absent.*

While there may be quite a few children in your group who won't initially understand the idea of finding the difference, you'll return to this activity many times over the next two months. Don't worry that some students seem a bit lost when you get to numbers beyond their current counting range, or seem confused when you work with them to determine how many youngsters are absent, if any. These initial efforts help children count and read numbers to twenty and beyond, and begin to plant many seeds for future understandings.

. . . .

A Link Each School Day & Our Month in School

Skills

★ counting by 1's

★ instant recognition of quantities to 5

★ recognizing "1 more"

★ seeing quantities in relationship to 5 and to 10

You'll need

★ the 1" × 7" paper strips

★ glue

★ Ten-Frame Dot cards

★ helper jar

Once the Kid Count has been made and you've determined how many (if any) children are absent today, direct children's attention to the task of recording

Day 3 Introducing the December Daily Routines (cont.)

the number of days they've been in school this month. Select a helper to attach a new link to the paper chain for December. As he's working, show students the new card for the Our Month in School chart. How many dots do they see on the card? How do they know? (This may seem like an obvious question, especially for a quantity as small as 3, but children's responses may be surprisingly varied.)

Teacher Here's the card for Our Month in School chart. How many spots do you see today?

Katie 3! it's just 1, 2, 3.

Teacher Do the rest of you agree?

Children It's 3, all right.
Yep, 3!

Teacher How do you know for sure?

Children I can just count on my fingers: 1, 2, 3.
I don't even have to count—I just know it's 3.
I can tell from the other cards in those pockets. There's 1 spot, then 2—this one has to be 3.
If there were 2 more spots, it would be the whole row full—5.
All the other rows are still empty.
We're going to get more and more spots on those cards, right?

Day 4

CALENDAR COMPONENTS

Introducing the December Daily Routines

It's the fourth school day in December, and all the Daily Routines are on their way to being established for the month. Enhance the Calendar Grid routine today a bit by adding a marker that signals the last day of school before Winter Break. Many of your children will be eager, both today and in the days to come, to count how many days until vacation. Also, add a set of cards to the Kid Count that literally puts the counting numbers into children's hands. With these two additions to the routines, you'll be well launched into the month of December.

. . . .

The Calendar Grid How Many Days 'Til Winter Break?

Skills

★ reading and extending an ABC pattern

★ counting and reading numerals

★ exploring duration on the calendar

You'll need

★ December calendar markers

★ Winter Break marker, placed in the appropriate pocket of your calendar grid

★ December pattern strip

★ helper jar

More than likely, as you gather children to the Number Corner today, someone will ask about the Winter Break card. If not, draw students' attention to the card and explain that you've placed it on the calendar to mark the last day of school before Winter Break. After they've determined which of the three quilt blocks should be posted for today, use the Winter Break card to help students figure out how long it will be until the last day of school before winter break.

Children *What's that snowman doing on our calendar?*
I made a snowman with my brothers.
I hope it snows today.
My dad said it might snow tonight!

Teacher *I put this marker with the snowman on it to mark the last day of school before Winter Break.*

Maxine *I see a W on that card. It's W for Winter Break, right?*

Day 4 Introducing the December Daily Routines (cont.)

Teacher *You're absolutely correct. Today, we're going to use this card to help us figure out how many days it will be until Winter Break starts. First, though, we need to post today's marker. Which quilt block will we need today, and what number will it have on it?*

Children *6—it's the number 6, 'cause 6 is right after 5—1, 2, 3, 4, 5, 6! It's going to be a Tic Tac Toe.*
No, it's going to be one of those stair-stepper ones. They always come right after the soccer balls.
It goes Tic Tac Toe, soccer ball, stair steps. Yep—stairs today.

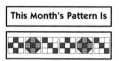

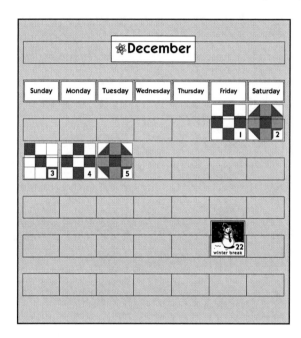

After children have had a chance to make some predictions, hang the new marker on the grid and then use your helper jar to choose a student to come to the grid and point to each box as children count how many days until the last day of school.

· ·

The Kid Count Adding the Number Cards

Skills

★ counting by 1's

★ using 1-to-1 correspondence

★ reading numbers to 20 and beyond

You'll need

★ the Kid Count chart, with the numbers from yesterday and the day before still circled

★ Kid Count number cards

Once the new marker for the day has been posted and children have had a chance to consider how many days are left until Winter Break, have them form a circle as near the counting chart as possible. Explain that after the Kid

Day 4 Introducing the December Daily Routines (cont.)

Count today, you're going to give them some cards to hold that will help them learn even more about numbers.

Begin the activity with the clap and count around the circle sequence you've done the last two days. How many children are present today? Can they find that number on the counting chart? Can they use the chart or some other method to figure out how many children, if any, are absent?

Then give each child a Kid Count number card to hold. Distribute the cards in random fashion and ask children to help each other figure out what their number card says. Is there anything on the cards that would help them figure out an unknown number? Once they've had a chance to look over their cards, explain that you want to line them up, one at a time, in order, with their cards. (If you have the space to line them up in a semicircle, they'll be able to see the cards more easily.) Which number should come first? Who is holding it? What number comes next? What numbers will the next three people be holding?

Stop and read the numbers periodically, and then add two or three more children until everyone is in the line. Ask students to hold up their number cards one at a time and read the numbers together. Then have several helpers collect the cards as you gather the group in the Number Corner for one last brief activity.

. . . .

The Paper Chain & the Our Month in School Chart

Skills
★ counting by 1's
★ instant recognition of quantities to 5
★ recognizing "1 more"
★ seeing quantities in relationship to 5 and to 10

You'll need
★ the 1" × 7" paper strips
★ glue
★ Ten-Frame Dot cards
★ helper jar

After the children have regrouped in the Number Corner, direct their attention to the paper chain and the Our Month in School chart. Select a helper to

Day 4 Introducing the December Daily Routines (cont.)

quickly attach a new link to December's paper chain. As she's working, hold up the new pocket chart card. How many dots do children see on the card? How do they know? (Again, this is a wonderful opportunity to develop children's sense of small quantities. Can they recognize 4 instantly when they see it? How does it compare with 5? With 10? What relation does this card bear to the three cards already in the chart?)

Teacher *Here's the card for the Our Month in School chart. What do you notice about it?*

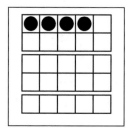

Ligia *It has 4 spots—1, 2, 3, 4.*

Teacher *Do you all agree with Ligia?*

Children *It's 4—I just know it.*
I know 'cause it's 2 and then 2 more. 2 and 2 makes 4.
It has to be 4, 'cause that's next after 3. The cards are counting 1 more, 1 more.
If there was 1 more, you'd see 5 spots.

Teacher *That's an interesting observation. How many more dots would there need to be on this card to make 10?*

Children *I know! 1 and then 5 more—it'd be 6.*
Can we count the boxes to see?

Teacher *Sure—why don't you come and point to them, David, and we'll all count.*

Children *1, 2, 3, 4, 5, 6—6 more to get up to 10.*
I can just see that it needs 1 more and then 5 more on the bottom—6!

Activities like these give children continual opportunities to solve problems in many different ways. Some children will use one-by-one counting to handle nearly every challenge this year. You'll find, though, that as you continue to encourage students to share their thinking—sometimes simply by asking how they can be sure of something, or by asking if they agree with a classmate's answer—youngsters will demonstrate a variety of strategies, and learn a great deal from one another in the process.

Day 5

CALENDAR COMPONENTS

Continuing Through December

The Daily Routines for December—the new calendar pattern, the Kid Count (with and without the number cards), the paper chain, and new cards for the Our Month in School chart—have been introduced. Hopefully, these activities are going smoothly enough to be compressed into 10-minute sessions several days a week as you return to the lessons in the *Bridges* Guide. Again, the key to keeping the Number Corner sessions short is to be selective. Although you'll want to post the new calendar marker, the new paper chain link, and the new ten-frame dot card every day, you can have a student helper do this for you on the days you're not able to get to them. The Kid Count only needs to happen once or twice a week. There may be days you choose to focus in depth on one or two of the routines, and days you run through all four at a brisk pace. Here are some ideas to consider as you use the Number Corner routines.

· ·

The Calendar Grid

• Continue to have children predict what the new calendar marker will be, using the pattern strip to help as necessary.

• Continue to count the days left until Winter Break, using the special marker posted on the calendar grid. You may find that some of your children begin to head straight for the calendar grid as they walk in to count the number of days.

• Use the markers as an ongoing source of counting and numeral recognition.

• Continue to model how to read the day and date every so often:
Today is _____, December _____, _____.
Be sure to point to the day name, the month, the marker number, and the year label as you chant the date.

• Have children practice writing the numerals for the day's date in the air, on the rug, on individual white boards or chalkboards.

Day 5 Continuing Through December (cont.)

• Once every week or so, have children practice tracing and writing a number in pencil or felt marker. Run copies of the appropriate Numeral Writing Practice page (Blacklines NC 6–NC 15) for this activity.

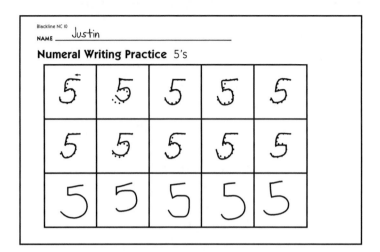

The Kid Count

• A very short version of this activity is simply to have children clap and count around the circle to determine how many students there are in class.

• If you want to devote more time to the activity, have children count and clap around the circle and find the number on the Kid Count chart. You might use a red overhead marker to circle the number on the chart that shows how many students are normally enrolled in your class, and use it as a reference point in helping youngsters figure out how many are absent on any given day.

The Kid Count chart

1	2	3	4	5	6	7	8	9	10
11	12	13	14	15	16	17	18	19	20
21	22	23	24	(25)	26	27	28	29	30
31	32	33	34	35	36	37	38	39	40

• On the days that you hand out the Kid Count number cards and have children line up holding their cards in order, you might also ask them to set their cards on the floor and step away from them, if space permits. Then turn four

Day 5 Continuing Through December (cont.)

or five of the cards face down while students close their eyes. Can they figure out which numbers are hidden?

A Link Each School Day How Many Days Have We Been in School This Month?

• Continue asking a helper to add a loop to the chain each day. When ten loops are in place, change colors and start the second group of ten. Once or twice during the month, you might bring the yearlong chain over to the Number Corner and have children count all the links by 10's and 1's, and then by 1's, to determine how many days they've spent in kindergarten, including the days in December.

Our Month in School Ten-Frame Dot Cards

• Continue adding a ten-frame dot card to the Our Month in School chart each day. Once or twice a week, you might want to have an extended discussion about how many dots are on the card for that day and encourage children to share their strategies for determining the total.

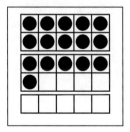

Children *Wow! There are lots of dots on that one.*
It has to be 16—we had 15 yesterday.
I know it's 16 because there are 10 on top and then 6 on the bottom.
I just go 10—11, 12, 13, 14, 15, 16, it's 16.
I know that 5 and 5 is 10, and then it's 6 more—16.
I go 5, 10, 15. Then 1 more is 16.
Can we count it the real way?

Day 5 Continuing Through December (cont.)

Counting things the "real way" may continue to be one by one for many, if not most of your children, well into first grade. It's interesting, though, that if you ask them to share the ways in which they're determining the total number of dots, some of your students will have other methods. As youngsters put their ideas into words, some of their classmates also begin to move toward counting on, counting by 5's and 10's, beginning to think of numbers as they relate to the nearest 5 or 10, and starting to see quantities in terms of smaller amounts that can be combined, such as 5 and 5, then 5 more and 1 more.

january

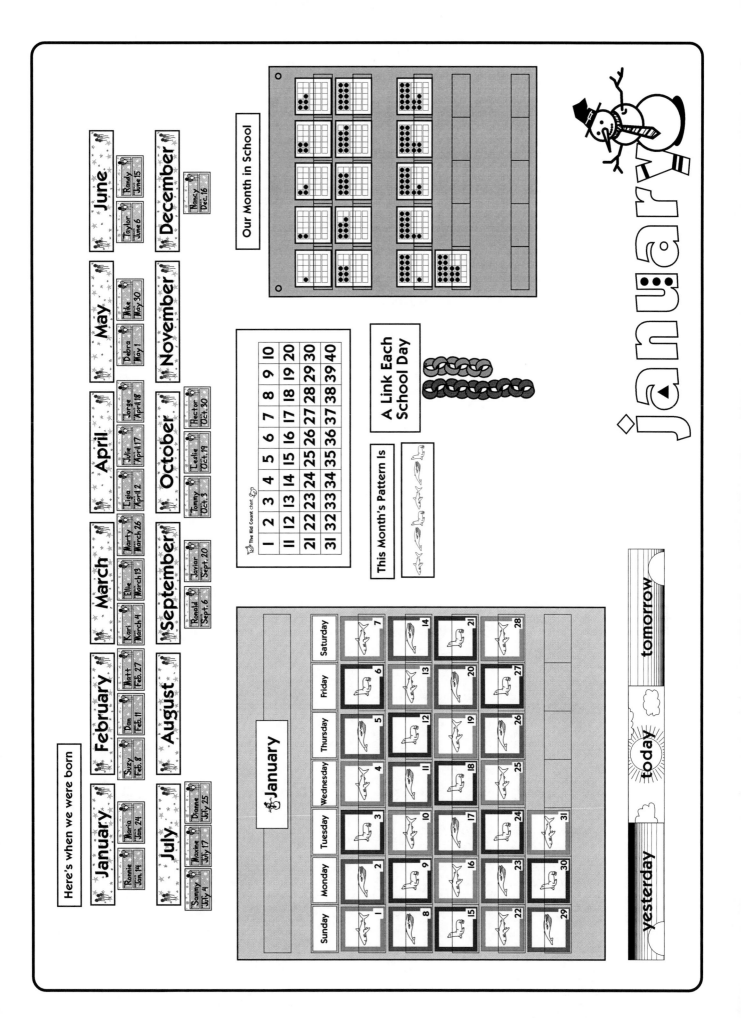

Here's when we were born

January · February · March · April · May · June

July · August · September · October · November · December

Our Month in School

The Kid Count chart

1	2	3	4	5	6	7	8	9	10
11	12	13	14	15	16	17	18	19	20
21	22	23	24	25	26	27	28	29	30
31	32	33	34	35	36	37	38	39	40

A Link Each School Day

This Month's Pattern Is

January

yesterday · today · tomorrow

Introduction

Welcome to the New Year! If you are using the full *Bridges* program with your kindergartners, you may be launching into Volume Two quite soon. Because the first thirty lessons in the second volume feature sea creatures as a focus for sorting, graphing, counting, and computation, we've designated sharks, whales, and seals as the new calendar markers. Even if you aren't using the *Bridges* lessons, you will find that your students respond eagerly to this theme, especially with the addition of the fact-filled songs you'll find in the Poems & Songs Portfolio. In addition to the new markers this month, you'll find another version of the Kid Count, this one set to music; a new set of dot cards for the Our Month in School chart designed to help children learn about odd and even numbers; and an entirely new component, the Yesterday, Today, Tomorrow card, useful for exploring concepts of yesterday, today, and tomorrow.

Note Even though you may feel like clearing away every trace of the prebreak madness before the new year begins, you'll need to leave your December calendar, complete with all 31 markers, up for one more day. Shifting this display and learning the new routines will take all of your math time for the first three days back to school. After that, as in previous months, the Number Corner routines will compress to about 10 minutes a day and may be done as part of your math instruction or daily opening. Once the Daily Routines smooth out, return to the Problems & Investigations lessons and Work Places in your Bridges *Guide, or continue with any other math program you may be using.*

· ·

The Calendar Grid

This month, we've provided blackline drawings of three different sea creatures for children to color and wash with watercolors.

Once they've made the markers, students will begin to post them on the calendar grid, following the ABCABC pattern shown on the January pattern strip. You may want to make a point of sharing one song a day—three in all—about the animals that appear in this pattern, especially if you're using the full *Bridges* program.

Seals & Sea Lions

(to the tune of "Twinkle, Twinkle, Little Star")

Seals and sea lions in the sea
Eating fish, sea birds, and squid.
They have sharp teeth but cannot chew,
Some have ears but not all do.
Seals and sea lions in the sea
Eating fish, sea birds, and squid.

This is an ideal time to find out what children already know about these animals and supply them with some of the factual information they'll need to solve and pose interesting sea creature story problems in the full *Bridges* program later in the month.

The Yearlong Paper Chain & A Link Each School Day

As January opens, children will count the links they collected in December and then add them to the yearlong chain in order to determine how many days they've been in kindergarten so far. To help students continue to move in the direction of being able to count the links in 10's and 1's, you'll hang labels at the end of each group of 10, as shown:

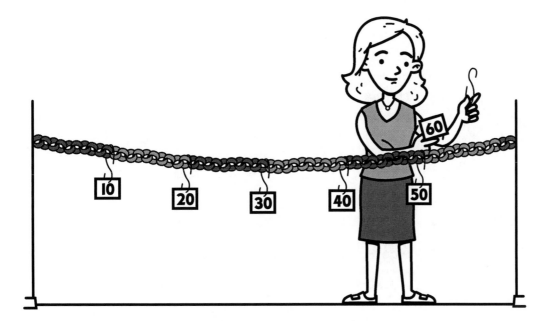

As in previous months, the children will continue to collect new links through January, which they'll add to the yearlong chain at the beginning of February.

Our Month in School

Like last month, children will post cards in the pocket chart that show a growing number of dots—one for each school day. Unlike last month's cards, though, this set is designed to provide a visual model of odd and even numbers. Because the dots have been grouped by 2's whenever possible, students are able to see that in some cases, all of the dots have partners, while in others, there's a dot left over with no partner.

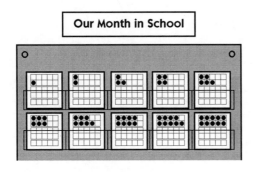

While the formal definition of even and odd numbers (numbers that either do or don't have 2 as a factor) is a bit beyond kindergartners, even young children quickly learn to identify quantities that can't be arranged in pairs as an odd number, and quantities in which all of the items can be paired, as an even number.

The Kid Count

This month, the now-familiar routine of clapping and counting around the circle to determine how many children are in class is enhanced with a song that sets the counting numbers from 1 to 20 to a pronounced beat. In this version of the activity, the children, each holding a Kid Count number card, line up in order, sit down where they are, and then stand back up and hold up their card when their number is sung. If you have students who are still struggling to learn the counting sequence to 20 and beyond, you may find that "The Number Rock," another song from *Songs for Number Corner by Greg and Steve*, is just the ticket.

Yesterday, Today & Tomorrow

This new routine is designed to help children begin to discuss and understand the language and concepts of past, present, and future. It revolves around a card with three headings—yesterday, today, and tomorrow. While this card will be used in several different ways through the remainder of the school year, this month's version involves a display of class art projects or worksheets, one under each heading. As students discuss the display each day, they have a chance to reflect on the passage of time.

> **Children** *That's funny! It has that pattern block snowflake by the tomorrow sign, but we made snowflakes today!*
> *And we didn't do any number writing today. We did those numbers before—yesterday.*
> *We did the sharks and whales a while ago. They're up on the calendar. Mine's not up there yet.*
> *I think we should move some of that stuff!*
>
> **Teacher** *It sounds like you're a bit puzzled by what you see on the Yesterday, Today, Tomorrow card today. Dianna even suggested that we move some of the things up here. What would you suggest, Dianna?*
>
> **Dianna** *Well, move the snowflake to today, 'cause we did those today. We're not going to do them tomorrow are we?*
>
> **Teacher** *No. If I move the snowflake, what should I do with Ella's number paper?*

Children *Give it back to her.*
No, I know! Move it to the yesterday spot. We did our numbers yesterday, not today.

Teacher *And what should we do with the shark marker?*

Children *Give it back to the Tommy!*
Put it up by your desk—it's pretty.
Save it for the calendar.

Teacher *You think I should take it off the Yesterday, Today, Tomorrow card, though? So if I make the moves you've suggested, the card will look a little different.*

Tomorrow, we're going to make snow people. You can make yours a boy or a girl, and give him or her any kind of hat you want. You can think about it when you go home today and bring your ideas with you when you come back tomorrow.

Notes

Day I

CALENDAR COMPONENTS

Introducing the January Daily Routines

To open the first school day of the new year, students clap and count to see if everyone's back in class. Then they begin to shift the Number Corner display into January, first counting the links collected in December, adding them to the yearlong paper chain, and attaching cards to the end of each color group to help them count the entire collection by 10's and 1's. Then they count the number of markers on the calendar grid to determine how many days there were in the month of December and when the last day of the month occurred. During this part of the lesson, remove the quilt blocks from the grid. Finally, the children use crayons and a watercolor wash to create sea creature markers for January.

. . . .

Note If you have a favorite theme already planned for the month, feel free to adapt the instructions in this lesson so children can make calendar markers that will better fit your plans. Because the upcoming Bridges lessons will ask students to pose and solve story problems about sea creatures, the markers we've suggested feature three of the seafaring animals from the Sea Creatures bucket—sharks, whales, and seals. Even if you're not using the full Bridges program, we think your children will engage happily with this theme. Along with blacklines to help your children create the sea creature markers for this month, you'll find some fact-filled songs in the Poems & Songs Portfolio that will help students become a bit more familiar with each of the three animals.

. . . .

Day I Introducing the January Daily Routines (cont.)

. . . .

The Kid Count

Skills

★ counting by I's

★ using I-to-I correspondence

★ reading numbers to 20 and beyond

★ exploring the idea of finding the difference

You'll need

★ the Kid Count chart (with the number that shows your class total already circled)

★ overhead marking pen

★ short pointer or hand puppet

Open today's session in the Number Corner by gathering the children into a circle. Ask them to clap and count around the circle as they learned to do last month. Go through the count twice just to double-check, and then have them locate that number on the Kid Count chart. How does it compare with the class total? Are all the children in class today, or are some absent? How many are missing, if any?

> **Children** *23! We got that number both times.*
> *Ronnie's gone today—I know 'cause he wasn't on the bus.*
> *24, 25—I think 2 kids are gone today.*

> **Teacher** *I'm so glad you're here today. Let's look at the number that's circled on our counting chart. This number tells how many children we have when everyone's here. Does anyone remember what it says?*

> **Children** *It's the 2 and the 5.*
> *25—25 is our number, but today we only have 23.*
> *23—24, 25, that's just 2.*
> *It's Ronnie and Dianna. She was gone from our carpool.*

Day I Introducing the January Daily Routines (cont.)

Use the Kid Count chart to help children determine how many students are absent today, if any.

The Kid Count chart

1	2	3	4	5	6	7	8	9	10
11	12	13	14	15	16	17	18	19	20
21	22	(23)	24	(25)	26	27	28	29	30
31	32	33	34	35	36	37	38	39	40

Teacher   How far is it from 23 to 25?

Children   Those 2 numbers are real close.
There's only one in the middle—so 1 kid is gone, right?
But Ronnie and Dianna are both gone—2 kids are missing, not 1!

Teacher   This is an interesting problem. We can only see 1 number between the 23 and the 25, but we know that 2 children are absent.

Joshua   But you have to go 24, 25. That's 1, 2—2 kids gone.

Teacher   Joshua is saying that we have to count from 23 all the way to 25 to determine the difference. Let's try it his way.

Children and Teacher   23—24, 25.

Although counting on to find the difference, especially between two quantities over 20, may still be confusing to some of your students, time and repeated opportunities to address the problem in this context will bring about understanding. Even children who don't comprehend the process of finding differences are learning to count and read numbers above 20 unless you have a very small class.

Day I Introducing the January Daily Routines (cont.)

. . . .

The Yearlong Paper Chain & A Link Each School Day

Skills

★ counting by I's

★ counting by 10's and I's

★ reading numbers above 10

You'll need

★ yearlong paper chain

★ the links you collected in December

★ I″ × 7″ construction paper strips (continue to use the same 2 colors)

★ scissors and glue

★ Paper Chain Number Labels up through 70 or 80, with large paper clips attached, as shown on left.

Once the Kid Count has been concluded, direct children's attention to the paper chain links they collected in December. How many 10's are displayed? Are there any additional 1's? How many links are there in all for the month of December? Count them one by one with the children and remove them from the calendar display. Then work with students to attach these links to the yearlong chain. As in previous months, you might have to do a little cutting and gluing, and perhaps some color switching to create all the possible groups of 10. As you work, you might want to review how many links there were in the yearlong chain at the end of November and ask them to estimate the total once the December links are added. More than likely, many children will respond with the number 100, which seems to be kindergarten code for "a lot," but you may encounter a few surprises.

> *Teacher* *There were 62 links in our yearlong chain at the end of November and now we're adding 16. How many do you think we'll have in all when the links are combined?*

> *Children* *A lot!*
> *100 is what I think.*
> *Me too—really a lot.*
> *That chain is way longer than me. It looks longer than Mrs. Holsberry.*
> *I think it'll be 70 and some more 'cause I counted those colors of 10.*
> *10, 20, 30, 40, 50, 60, 70—and the extra 1's.*

When all of the possible 10's have been combined, have a student help you stretch the chain out on the floor, and then work with children's help to label the last link in each color group with one of the new Paper Chain Number Labels.

Day I Introducing the January Daily Routines (cont.)

Now that the chain is labeled, can anyone figure out how many links there are altogether? After giving students a minute to think about the problem, count the links by 10's, pointing to the number labels as the children count with you. When you reach the 1's, point to each individual link carefully as you count them. Then ask children to count the links again with you, stretching their hands out to show 10 fingers for each group of 10 and then clapping when you reach the 1's. (These finger motions provide a tactile experience each time the children name one of the numbers in the counting-by-10's sequence. Clapping on the 1's breaks the sequence and alerts children to the change, even if they don't fully understand it.)

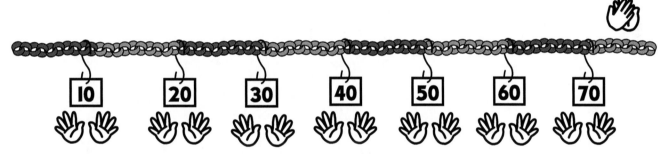

If you feel that you have the time, you might want to go back and count the chain once more by 1's to help children confirm the total. (For many of your students, counting by 1's will continue to be the "real way" to determine a total well into first grade.) If this seems too time-consuming for now, however, leave it until another day.

Finally, select a helper to construct the first paper link for January, and attach it to the Link Each School Day label.

As the helper is working, take a look at the Here's When We Were Born chart. Was anyone born today? Does anyone have a birthdate coming up in January? How many children in class were born in January?

Day I Introducing the January Daily Routines (cont.)

. . . .

The Calendar Grid One Last Look at December

Skills
★ reading an ABC pattern

★ counting by I's to 3I

★ naming the days of the week

You'll need
★ Days of the Week song

★ completed December calendar grid

★ a 5″ × 5″ piece of construction paper in a bright color

Before you dismantle December's calendar grid, have the children read through the entire month's pattern as a helper points to each marker. Then as a second helper points to the markers again, have students recite each of the counting numbers. Finally, sing the Days of the Week song for the entire month, quickly removing each of the markers from the grid as the days are named. When you get to the last marker, stop singing. What day *was* that? Then slip a brightly colored square of construction paper into the pocket in the top row of the now-empty grid under the very next day to help everyone remember the starting point for posting the new markers, once they're made.

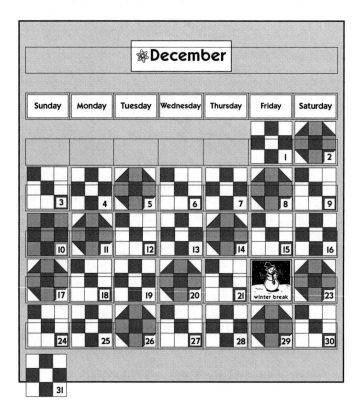

Teacher On which day did December end?

Children Sunday!
This month starts on Monday.
1 goes on Monday.
It has to be Monday—that's what comes next in the song after Sunday.

Day I Introducing the January Daily Routines (cont.)

Teacher *We won't have enough room for our new markers on this grid if we have to start way at the bottom, so we'll have to go back up to the top row and find the pocket that comes under Monday there. Does anyone see the word "Monday" along the top of the grid?*

Children *It's the one with M.*
Just like my name—Mike starts with M! Just find my letter!

Teacher *You're right, and I'm going to mark this pocket with a big square of colored paper to help us remember where to start posting our new markers when we get them made.*

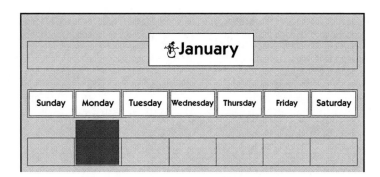

The Calendar Grid Making the New Markers

Skills

★ observing and describing

You'll need

★ January Calendar Markers, sheets I–2 (Blackline NC I9–NC 20, run II–22 copies on white paper or cardstock and cut apart. You'll only need 31 markers for the calendar—II sharks, 10 whales, and 10 seals. If you teach double session, though, you'll still want each child to make a marker.)

★ crayons

★ watercolor brushes, containers of water, and watercolors (optional)

★ a book, or books, that have colored illustrations or photos of seals, sharks, and whales

★ 3I 5″ squares of construction paper, I0 in each of 2 different colors and II in a third color to back the children's sea creature markers

Day 1 Introducing the January Daily Routines (cont.)

Now that the old markers have been removed from the calendar grid, it's time to make new ones. Show children the pictures of sea creatures you've prepared for them to color (see below). Can they name any of the three?

The first is a shark, the second is a whale, and the third is a seal. Take a minute to look at some colored photos or sketches of these three animals so that children have a sense of their true coloration, and then send them out to work. Unless you teach two sessions, a few of your students will probably have to color in more than one marker. If you do have two groups, ask all the children to color in a marker, and plan to use the extras for students to pattern on their own during Work Places, or for some other purpose.

After they've colored in the animals, you may want to have youngsters do a watercolor wash to lend the markers an ocean-like look. The easiest way we've found to do this is to have children use watercolor brushes to paint the markers with *water only*, first, and then with colors from an ordinary tray of watercolor paints.

Washing over the markers with water first will prevent students from painting over the colored animals so heavily that they're not visible. However, in case of disaster, if you catch the problem while the marker is still wet, use a paper towel to blot up the extra color. You might have everyone in class wash their markers with blue, green, turquoise, purple—ocean-like colors. *We ask our children not to use brown or black.*

• •

Note *You'll need to do a couple more things to prepare the calendar markers for tomorrow's lesson. Once they've dried thoroughly, you may want to outline each of the sea creatures in black, using a permanent marker, to make them show up more clearly. This may be particularly important if a few of your students don't color accurately yet. You'll also need to glue all of the sharks to 5" squares of colored construction paper in one color, all of the whales to squares in a second color, and all of the seals to construction paper squares in a third color. You'll need 11 shark markers, 10 whales, and 10 seals in order to be able to create an ABC pattern for the month. Finally, you'll need to decide if you want to number the markers ahead of time or engage children in numbering them each day. (Some teachers run a copy of Blacklines NC 2–NC 3, cut the numbers apart, and keep them pinned to the board or displayed in some way so that students have an opportunity to search through the collection and find the number that's needed for the marker each day as it's posted on the grid .)*

• •

Color A
Backing

Color B
Backing

Color C
Backing

Day 2

CALENDAR COMPONENTS

Introducing the January Daily Routines

It's the second school day of January and the new calendar markers are ready to go. Introduce the pattern for the month, along with a song about the first animal in the pattern—the shark. Next, do the Kid Count, and after determining how many children are in class, hand out the Kid Count number cards, and have students line up in order. Then add a link to January's paper chain and share a new set of number cards for the Our Month in School chart. Finally, introduce the Yesterday, Today, Tomorrow card, a new addition to the Number Corner that will give children an opportunity to explore the idea of yesterday, today, and tomorrow.

· ·

The Calendar Grid Getting Started

Skills

★ reading and extending an ABC pattern

★ gathering information from pictures and text

You'll need

★ January markers children made yesterday

★ January pattern strip (If you're using markers for a different theme, you'll need to make a pattern strip to fit.)

★ Calendar Numbers sheets 1–2 (Blackline NC 2–NC 3, run 1 copy of each)

★ Shark song (Poems & Songs Portfolio A, pages PA.20–PA.25, use the pages to create a wall chart or bind them together to make a big book)

Open today's session by inviting children to join you in the discussion area. Post the new pattern strip and ask students what they notice. Can they name any of the sea creatures? Read the pattern together.

Which sea creature will have to be posted first on the calendar grid, and where? It's the second school day of the month, but it may be the 3rd or 4th of January, or even later, depending on the timing of your winter break. With children's help, figure out how many markers need to be displayed to bring

Day 2 Introducing the January Daily Routines (cont.)

the calendar grid up to date. If you haven't already glued numbers to the markers, the students will also need to help you with this task.

Before you move on, you might introduce the Shark song to your students. Ask them to gather at least one piece of information about sharks as they listen to you sing it through once or twice. Then have them sing along as you sing it a third time. What did they learn about sharks from the song?

Sharks
(to the tune of "Did You Ever See a Lassie?")

Did you ever see a shark,
a shark, a shark,
Did you ever see a shark
with a fin on its back

And two on its sides
For balance as it glides?

Did you ever see a shark
with a fin on its back?

Day 2 Introducing the January Daily Routines (cont.)

. . . .

The Kid Count

Skills

★ counting by 1's

★ using 1-to-1 correspondence

★ reading numbers to 20 and beyond

You'll need

★ the Kid Count chart with the class total still circled

★ Kid Count number cards

After they've updated the calendar grid, have children form a circle in the Number Corner to do the Kid Count. Begin the activity with the familiar clap and count around the circle sequence. How many children are present today? Can they find that number on the counting chart? Can they use the chart or some other method to figure out how many children, if any, are absent?

Then distribute the Kid Count number cards in random fashion, one per child, and ask children to help each other figure out what their number cards say. Is there anything on the cards that would help them figure out an unknown number? Once they've had a chance to look over their cards, explain that you want them to line them up, one at a time, in order, with their cards. (If you have the space to line them up in a semicircle, the children will be able to see their classmates' cards more easily.) Which number should come first? Who is holding it? What number comes next? What numbers will the next three people be holding?

Stop and read the numbers periodically, and then have more children join the line, two or three at a time, until they're all standing. Ask students to hold up their number cards one at a time and have everyone read the numbers together. Then have several helpers collect the cards as you regroup the children in front of the calendar.

. . . .

A Link Each School Day How Many Days Have We Been in School This Month?

Skills

★ counting by 1's

★ counting by 10's

★ adding "1 more"

You'll need

★ the 1" × 7" paper strips

★ glue

Next, direct students' attention to the A Link Each School Day display. How many school days have passed in January so far? Select a helper to construct a new paper link for today.

Day 2 Introducing the January Daily Routines (cont.)

Our Month in School Introduce the Ten-Frame Odd & Even Cards

Skills

★ exploring odd and even numbers

★ counting by 1's

★ instant recognition of quantities to 5

★ recognizing "1 more"

You'll need

★ Ten-Frame Odd & Even cards

★ helper jar

Once today's link has been posted, show children the new cards for the Our Month in School chart. Like last month's cards, these show growing collections of dots arranged in ten-frames. This time, however, the dots have been arranged to help students begin to explore odd and even numbers. As new dots are added from one day to the next, sets of two are completed, so the cards for the first four days look like this:

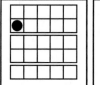

Have helpers post the first two cards in the chart and then ask children to share their observations.

Children *It goes 1, 2!*
There's 1 spot, and then 2.
It's like last time, but these dots are blue.
It's just like counting—I bet 3 comes tomorrow.
It's a new dot for each day, right?

After students have commented on the cards, take a moment to introduce the idea of odd and even. Explain that the quantity on the first card—1— shows an odd number, and that the quantity on the second card shows an even number. (Simply defined, an odd number does not have 2 as a factor, and an even number does. This is a bit beyond kindergartners. However,

Day 2 Introducing the January Daily Routines (cont.)

even young children are quite intrigued with the idea, and quickly learn to identify quantities that can't be arranged in pairs as odd, and quantities in which all of the items can be paired, as even.)

Teacher *These cards are similar to the cards we had on the Our Month in School chart last month, but the dots are a different color, and they've been arranged differently. One thing you might have noticed about the first card is that the one little dot has no partner. People call 1 an odd number. On the second card, both dots have a partner, and 2 is called an even number. We're going to be talking lots about odd and even numbers this month. What kind of number do you think we'll see tomorrow when we put up the next card?*

Children *A 3!*
It's going to have 3 dots—I know it.
I can show on my fingers, see? 1, 2, 3.

Teacher *Tomorrow's card will have 3 dots, all right. Do you think 3 is an odd number, or an even number?*

Children *Odd?*
I don't know.
If there's 3, one of them can't have a partner.

One way to illustrate the idea of odd and even numbers is to match the students in pairs. Kindergartners are so exquisitely sensitive to issues of friendship—being included, having a hand to hold—that they grasp the concept very quickly this way.

Teacher *I'm going to pull 3 sticks out of the helper jar and ask those 3 children to stand up here beside the chart to help us out for a moment. Jody, Jorge, and Seth, will you join me? If Jorge and Jody hold hands, can Seth have a partner?*

Children *No, and he'll be sad.*
He could pick another kid to be his partner.
He could hold hands with them too, and all 3 of them could be partners.
I know! Seth could hold your hand, and then he'd have a partner.

Day 2 Introducing the January Daily Routines (cont.)

Teacher It's true that if we had 1 more person up here, Seth would be able to have a partner. How many children would there be if 1 more joined the group?

Children 1, 2, 3, 4—4 kids!
It would be those 3 and 1 more—that's 4.
With 4, everyone could have a partner.

Teacher So 4 is an even number, and 3 is odd.

This is a concept you'll revisit many times throughout the month, so don't worry if some of the children don't seem to understand yet.

. . . .

Yesterday, Today & Tomorrow

Skills
★ exploring the idea of yesterday, today, and tomorrow; past, present, and future

You'll need
★ Yesterday, Today, Tomorrow card (post in Number Corner display)

★ 3 pieces of artwork or other simple class projects or worksheets—I from yesterday, I children have done today, and I you plan to have them do tomorrow

★ scotch tape, stapler, or pins

To conclude today's Number Corner session, call attention to the Yesterday, Today, Tomorrow card you've posted. More than likely, they've already asked you about it, curious about the pictures and the words, wondering what it's for. Take a minute or two to discuss the simple drawings on the card and read the three words—Yesterday, Today, and Tomorrow. Explain that you're going to be using the card to keep track of projects and artwork you're doing in class this month.

Show a project the children did yesterday—perhaps you'll choose one of the extra calendar markers—and discuss it briefly. Have students review the things they did to complete the project. In the case of the calendar marker, they might remember that they colored in the sea creature, then washed it with watercolor, and then left it to dry. Tape this piece of work under the heading that reads "Yesterday" on the card. Repeat this procedure with a project that the children have already completed today, and one you plan to have them do tomorrow. After presenting each piece and talking with youngsters

Day 2 Introducing the January Daily Routines (cont.)

about it very briefly, tape it under the proper heading on the card. When you're finished, you'll have a very tangible illustration of past, present, and future—something the children did yesterday, something they did today, and something they'll be doing tomorrow.

. . . .

Note To avoid confusion between today and tomorrow, you might save the Yesterday, Today, Tomorrow card until the end of the morning or afternoon. This way, children will have completed some kind of project or worksheet that very day and won't become as confused as they might otherwise about the difference between doing something later today and doing something tomorrow.

. . . .

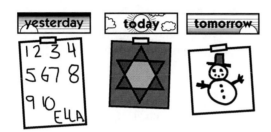

"Yesterday we practiced writing our numbers. Ella let me borrow her work to put up."
"Today we're going to make snowflake designs with pattern blocks to decorate the room."
"Tomorrow we're going to make snowpeople."

Day 3

 CALENDAR COMPONENTS

Introducing the January Daily Routines

It's the third school day of January. If you sang the Shark song with your children yesterday, they may have picked up new information about these creatures. If time permits today, you might share the Whale song and discuss some things that make sharks and whales alike and different. After today's marker is posted, children will learn a new song to accompany the Kid Count. "The Number Rock" is a great way to learn to count and read numbers to 20 and beyond. Finally, students work with you to post another paper chain link, a new Ten-Frame Odd & Even card, and return to the Yesterday, Today, Tomorrow card for a look at what happens when "tomorrow" becomes "today."

. . . .

The Calendar Grid What Comes Next?

Skills
★ reading and extending an ABC pattern
★ gathering information from pictures and text
★ comparing sharks and whales/fish and mammals

You'll need
★ calendar markers
★ January pattern strip
★ Calendar Numbers, unless you've already glued them to your markers
★ Whale song (Poems & Songs Portfolio A, pages PA.26–PA.29, use the pages to create a wall chart or bind them together to make a big book)

To begin today's session, ask children to join you in the Number Corner. Once they're settled, draw their attention to the calendar grid and have them name the animals on the markers that have already been posted. Then ask them to predict which animal they'll see on the marker today and share their ideas.

Teacher So far we've had a shark, a whale, and a seal on our calendar grid. Which animal will we see on today's marker?

Children Shark!
I think it's going to be the whale!
No, it has to be the shark.
Seal, it's the seal!
But we just had the seal yesterday

Teacher It sounds like some of you are pretty convinced that today's

Day 3 Introducing the January Daily Routines (cont.)

marker is going to be a shark, while others think it might be a whale or a seal. Would anyone be willing to tell us why they think it's going to be the shark, the seal, or the whale?

Kari *It has to be the shark, 'cause that's how the pattern goes—shark, whale, seal, shark, whale, seal. It even says up there on that strip.*

Randy *The shark always has to come next after the seal. It's shark today.*

Jesse *It could change. It could get to be the whale again.*

Teacher *So, you mean it could go shark, whale, seal, whale?*

Julie *That's not what it says on the pattern strip, though. If you look up there, you can see it's a shark today.*

Tommy *Patterns don't change—they just keep going and going.*

You may be surprised to discover that for some of your children the notion of a pattern as something that repeats again and again in a predictable manner is still a little shaky, especially if the sequence is more complex than ABABAB, or made more complicated by the fact that the repeating units shift sometimes from row to row on the grid. This is one of the reasons we find it so helpful to post a strip each month that shows the pattern in linear form.

After a bit of discussion, pull out today's marker and have a helper post it on the grid. Read the sequence on the calendar together just to make sure that it matches the pattern strip so far. Then take a minute to talk about the creatures themselves. If you have time, sing the Whale song to your class.

Day 3 Introducing the January Daily Routines (cont.)

Whales
(to the tune of "Are You Sleeping?")

Whales are swimming, whales are swimming,
They're headed south, they're headed south,
Seeking warmer water
To give birth to a baby,
Mothers and calves,
Mothers and calves.

Once they've heard the song, ask children to join in as you sing it a second time. Does the song tell them even more things about whales than they already knew? How are whales like sharks? How are they different?

. . . .

The Kid Count Doing the Number Rock

Skills

★ counting by 1's

★ using 1-to-1 correspondence

★ reading numbers to 20 and beyond

You'll need

★ Kid Count number cards

★ "The Number Rock" (You'll find this song on the cassette tape or CD, *Songs for Number Corner by Greg and Steve*)

After the calendar grid has been updated and you've taken a few minutes to discuss the creatures, possibly singing the Whale song, have children form a circle in the Number Corner to do the Kid Count. Begin the activity with the familiar clap and count around the circle sequence. Then distribute the Kid Count number cards in random fashion, one per child, and ask children to help each other figure out what their number cards say.

Day 3 Introducing the January Daily Routines (cont.)

Once they've had a chance to look over their cards, have students line up in order in a semicircle, if possible. Then have everyone sit down, right where they are, still holding their cards. Explain that you're all going to sing a song called The Number Rock that names the numbers from 1 to 20, and as children's numbers are called out, they're going to stand up. Play the song through once for everyone to hear. Then play it a second time and have students stand as their numbers are sung. If there are more than 20 in your group, you'll need to call out the remaining numbers at the end of the song so no one's left out of the line of standing children at the end.

When the song ends, you'll need to call out as many numbers as you have children still left sitting and holding number cards, so that everyone ends up standing in the end:

21, 22, 23, 24, 25, 26! (for instance)

When the song is over, have several helpers collect the cards as you regroup the children in front of the calendar.

· ·

The Yearlong Paper Chain & Our Month in School

Skills
★ counting by 1's
★ exploring odd and even numbers
★ instant recognition of quantities to 5
★ recognizing "1 more"

You'll need
★ the 1" × 7" paper strips
★ glue
★ Ten-Frame Odd & Even cards
★ helper jar

When everyone has settled again, direct children's attention to the task of recording the number of days they've been in school this month. Select a helper to attach a new link to the paper chain for January. As she's working, show students the new card for the Our Month in School chart. How many dots do they see on the card? Is the number odd or even? How do they know?

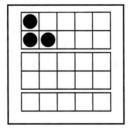

Children *It goes 1, 2, 3!*
It had to be 3 today, 'cause it was 1 and then 2 before.
There's 1 spot on top and 2 on the bottom.
1 plus 2 is 3.

Day 3 Introducing the January Daily Routines (cont.)

It looks like a foot.
No, like the big letter L!

Teacher   *You have some interesting observations about the card today. Is 3 an odd number or an even number?*

Ella   *Odd—it's odd! I remember from yesterday.*

Teacher   *What do you remember?*

Ella   *It's like when you had the kids stand up, and Seth didn't have a partner.*

Sammy   *It's like that 1 little dot sticking out doesn't have a partner— he's all alone.*

Maria   *Tomorrow it will be even, 'cause there will be a friend for that 1 little dot.*

Teacher   *You're right. 4 is an even number and 3 is odd. You remember lots about odd and even numbers.*

. . . .

Yesterday, Today & Tomorrow

Skills
★ understanding the idea of yester-day, today, and tomorrow; past, present, and future

You'll need
★ Yesterday, Today, Tomorrow card
★ a piece of artwork or other simple class project or worksheet you plan to have children do tomorrow
★ scotch tape

At the end of the Number Corner session, or, better yet, at the end of your kindergarten day, after the children have completed the project taped under the "Tomorrow" heading, take a few minutes to look again at the card. Read the three headings with children and then ask them to share any thoughts and observations they may have. If things don't seem to be arranged correctly on the card anymore, encourage students to suggest changes that will correct the situation. You may have to guide them a bit at first, although you'll notice that in the process of sharing their observations, the students in the discussion below begin to generate some questions and suggestions.

Children   *That's funny! It has that snowflake by the tomorrow sign, but we made snowflakes today!*
And we didn't do any number writing today. We did those numbers before—yesterday.

Day 3 Introducing the January Daily Routines (cont.)

We did the sharks and whales a while ago. They're on the calendar now.
I think we should move some of that stuff!

Teacher *It sounds like you're a bit puzzled by what you see on the Yesterday, Today, Tomorrow card today. Dianna even suggested that we move some of the things up here. What would you suggest, Dianna?*

Dianna *Well, move the snowflake to today, 'cause we did those today. We're not going to do them tomorrow are we?*

Teacher *No. If I move the snowflake, what should I do with Ella's number paper?*

Children *Give it back to her.*
No, I know! Move it to the yesterday spot. We did our numbers yesterday, not today.

Teacher *And what should we do with the shark marker?*

Children *Give it back to the kid who made it!*
Put it up by your desk—it's pretty.
Save it for the calendar.

Teacher *You think I should take it off the Yesterday, Today, Tomorrow card, though? So if I make the moves you've suggested, the card will look a little different.*

Once the necessary moves have been made, show children a project or paper you have planned for tomorrow and tape it under the correct heading. You may find as you use this card from day to day, that many of your students enjoy knowing something about what's planned for the following day. There may even be times when it's appropriate to involve the children themselves in a bit of planning, giving them a choice, for instance, between one project or another for the next day, and taping their selection under the "Tomorrow" heading.

Day 4

 CALENDAR COMPONENTS

Continuing Through January

By now, you've introduced all the daily routines for January—the new pattern on the Calendar Grid, the Kid Count (with and without the Number Rock song), A Link Each School Day, the Ten-Frame Odd & Even cards for the Our Month in School chart, and the new Yesterday, Today, Tomorrow card. Hopefully, these activities are going smoothly enough to be compressed into short 10-minute lessons several days a week as you return to your regular math instruction. Here are some ideas to consider in shaping your Number Corner sessions over the rest of the month.

The Calendar Grid

• Continue to have children predict what the new calendar marker will be each day, using the pattern strip to help as necessary. On the days you don't have time to get to the Number Corner, have a helper post the calendar marker, the paper chain link, and the Ten-Frame Odd & Even card.

• If you elected not to put the calendar numbers on ahead of time, display the rest of them, in random order on a nearby bulletin board, or even in the bottom few pockets of your calendar grid pocket chart. As the calendar marker goes up each day, have a helper locate the number that needs to be attached.

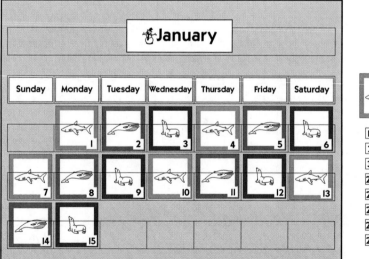

Teacher *What number needs to go on our marker today?*

Day 4 Continuing Through January (cont.)

Children 16—it's 16, 'cause 16 comes after 15!
Let's count and see for sure!
1, 2, 3, 4, 5, 6, 7, 8, 9, 10, 11, 12, 13, 14, 15, 16—yep! It's 16, all right.

Teacher *Mike, you're our helper today, and I'm going to ask you to come up here and find the 16 for us so we can glue it to the marker. Boys and girls, let's give Mike a little help. What should he look for when he comes up to search for the 16?*

Children *Look for a 1 and a 6.*
I see right where it is. Do you want me to help, Mike?
It's up near the top, right near the one that says 27.

• Once every week or so, you might want to return to the Days of the Week song. Also, you might introduce the Seals & Sea Lions song (Poems & Songs Portfolio A, pages PA.30–PA.33 and review the Sharks and Whales songs.

• Continue to model how to read the day and date every so often:
Today is _____, January _____, _____.
Be sure to point to the day name, the month, the marker number, and the year label as you chant the date.

• Have children practice writing the numerals for the day's date in the air, on the rug, on individual white boards or chalkboards, or on the appropriate Numeral Writing Practice sheets (Blacklines NC 6–NC 15).

• At the very end of the month, ask students to help you remove the odd numbered markers from the grid and look at the pattern that remains. (If they're not sure whether a particular number is odd or even, have them refer to the Ten-Frame Odd & Even cards on the Our Month in School chart.)

Children *Hey, look! It's all diagonal lines.*
It looks like stairs.
And see how it's all whales, and then all sharks, and then all seals, and then all whales again?

Teacher *Let's try reading the numbers on the markers that are left.*

Day 4 Continuing Through January (cont.)

Children *2, 4, 6, 8, 10 — it's the even numbers.*
It's counting by 2's!

The Kid Count

• A very short version of this activity is simply to have children clap and count around the circle to determine how many students there are in class.

• The Number Rock is a hit with most kindergartners, and many of your students will surely want to repeat this version of the Kid Count many times this month. One variation, once they're lined up with their number cards and are ready to sing, is to have them sit down when their numbers are sung. As soon as they're all down, rewind the tape, play it again, and have them stand up as their number is called as they sing the song a second time.

• If you want to devote more time to the activity, have children count and clap around the circle and find the number on the Kid Count chart. You might use a red overhead marker to circle the number on the chart that shows how many students are normally enrolled in your class, and use it as a reference point in helping youngsters figure out how many are absent on any given day.

• On the days that you hand out the Kid Count cards and have children line up holding their cards in order, you might also ask them to set their cards on the floor and step away from them, if space permits. Then turn four or five of the cards face down while students close their eyes. Can they figure out which numbers are hidden?

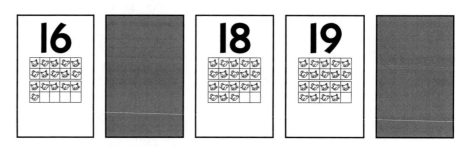

A Link Each School Day How Many Days Have We Been in School This Month?

• Continue asking a helper to add a link to the chain each day. When ten links are in place, change colors and start the second group of ten.

• Every so often during the month, you might have the children determine the total number of days they've been in kindergarten so far. Start by pointing to the counting-by-10's labels you attached to the yearlong chain at the begin-

Day 4 Continuing Through January (cont.)

ning of the month. Have the children count by 10's and show 10 fingers for each multiple of 10 as you point to the labels. When you get to the 1's at the end of the chain, have students clap and count by 1's. Ask them to continue clapping and counting by 1's as you move to the links that have been added for the month of January so far.

> **Teacher** *Great counting! How many days have we been in kindergarten so far this year?*

> **Children** *85!*

- -

Our Month in School Ten-Frame Odd & Even Cards

• Continue adding a Ten-Frame Odd & Even card to the Our Month in School chart each day.

Once or twice a week, you might want to have an extended discussion about how many dots are on the card for that day and encourage children to share their strategies for determining the total.

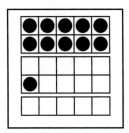

> **Children** *Wow! There are lots of dots on that one.*
> *It has to be 11—we had 10 yesterday.*
> *It's the same as the paper chain—11, 'cause we have 11 loops today.*
> *I know it's 11 because there are 10 on top and then 1 on the bottom—that's just 10, 11.*
> *I know 5 and 5 is 10, and then it's 1 more—11*

• Throughout the month, you'll want to engage students in discussions about odd and even numbers. You can do this by asking them to consider the arrangement of dots on a card. Does each dot on the card for a particular day have a partner? You can also guide children as they pair themselves to see if a number is odd or even.

> **Teacher** *Great job of figuring out how many dots are on this card. Tell me now, is 11 odd or even?*

> **Children** *There's a lot of spots on that card. It's kind of hard to tell.*
> *There's 1 dot without a partner, down on the bottom.*
> *There's 1 sticking out by itself. I think it's odd.*

Day 4 Continuing Through January (cont.)

Teacher *This card isn't very big, and there are a lot of dots on it. Let's try it with kids. I'm going to call you 1 by 1 as all of us count to keep track of how many children have come up to the front of the room. If your name is called, please come forward and look for a partner. Once you're paired up with someone, hold their hand. What will happen if 11 is an odd number?*

Sarah *Someone won't have a partner at the end. They'll be standing alone.*

Ronak *If it's even, all the kids will have a partner.*

- You might also want to have children conduct experiments with Unifix cubes to see if certain numbers are odd or even. To do this, have each student count out a number of cubes equivalent to the dots on the card for the day. Then have them each work to see if they can form groups of two with all of their cubes.

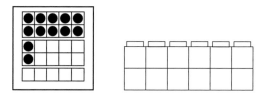

"When I use 12 cubes, they all get a partner. 12 must be even!"

Yesterday, Today & Tomorrow

As you continue to use the Yesterday, Today, Tomorrow card throughout the month, we think you and your class will enjoy the opportunity at the end of each day to review the projects you've done and look ahead to the next day. The discussions you'll have around this card will be rich in the grammar and vocabulary of past, present, and future, and the experience will help children begin to grasp the idea of yesterday, today, and tomorrow in a very tangible way.

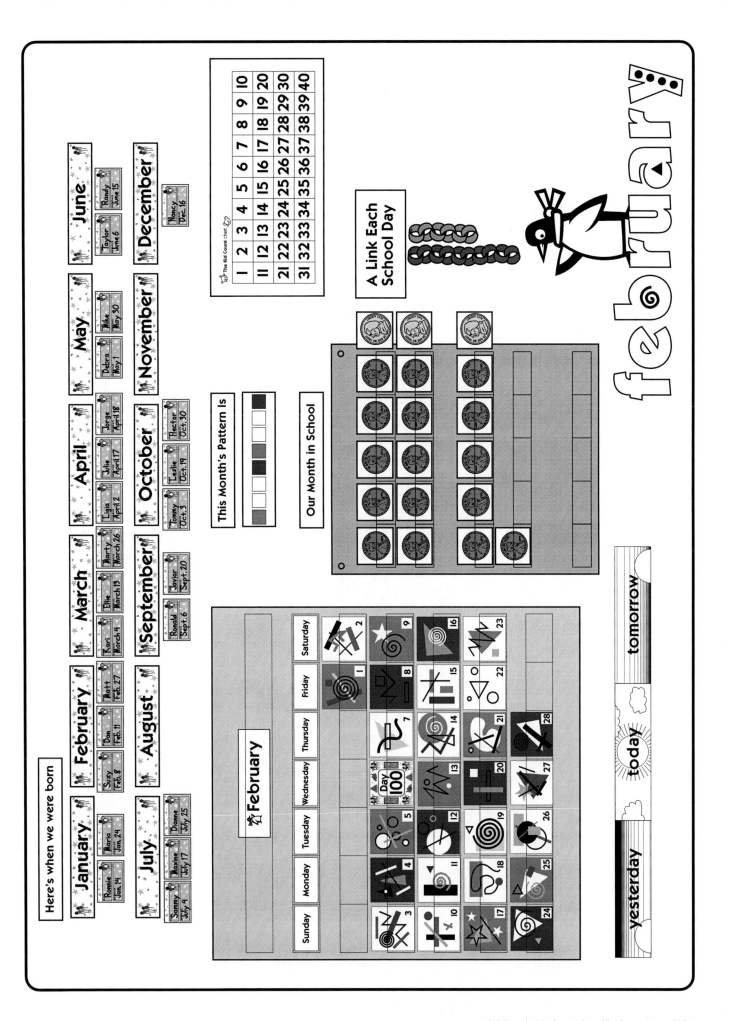

Introduction

Whether it's snowing and blowing, or you're basking in the warm desert sun, the big event of the kindergarten calendar year is fast approaching. The hundredth day of school, or Day 100, is celebrated only in kindergarten in the *Bridges* program, and you'll find some special activities to help celebrate this event with your students on pages 195–206. As in previous months, the first three sessions of this chapter are devoted to shifting the calendar display into the new month and introducing a couple of new Daily Routines. These sessions are followed by a set of suggestions for continuing the Daily Routines through February. At the end of the chapter, you'll find four special activities for Day 100. Each one of these requires a full math period or more, and although you might pack them all into one day if you teach a full- or extended-day kindergarten, you might be happier introducing them over several days. Another possibility is to choose one or two of the activities, rather than doing all four. These lessons are meant to be fun, flexible, and definitely optional, so do whatever suits you.

Note *As usual, you'll need to leave last month's calendar display up in order to do the first day's Number Corner activities. Shifting this display and learning the new routines will take all of your math time for the first three days in February. If your Day 100 lands on one of these days, you might either devote extra time to math, or delay getting started with some of the Daily Routines. Once the Daily Routines are established, you'll be able to ease back into the 10 minute Number Corner sessions.*

The Calendar Grid

Our suggestion for the calendar markers this month is to have children make miniature collages with paper strips glued to red, white, or blue backgrounds. If you show your students some paper folding and cutting techniques, some will produce pieces that are 3-dimensional. (If these don't fit into the pockets, just paper clip them on the fronts of the pockets.) Some children will enjoy simply gluing strips to their paper squares. These markers are fun to make, quite attractive, and because of the background colors, they lend themselves well to forming patterns.

The pattern this month is an ABBCABBC sequence (red, white, white, blue) and because it's fairly complex, we suggest that you set some hand and body motions to this pattern so that students literally get a feel for the sequence.

"red, white, white, blue"

You'll also find that the calendar grid provides sound opportunities for children to explore the passage of time this month. By marking Day 100 with a special card that's been included in your Number Corner materials, students will have a chance to visually track the days until the hundredth day of school. We've also suggested that you work with children to move the February birthdate markers onto the grid, counting to locate the pockets in which they belong. Marking these special occasions will give you a very meaningful context in which to discuss the names of the days, the numbers on the markers, and the weekly structure and layout of the grid itself.

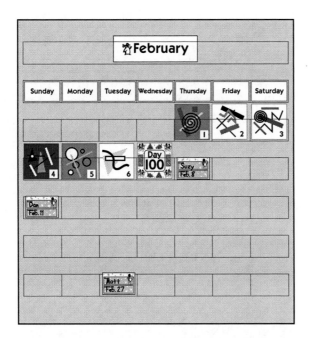

Children *Only 1 more day 'til Day 100. Is school over then?*
Suzy's birthday—it's only 2 more days.
It's a long time 'til Matt's birthday.

Teacher *What day of the week is Dan's birthday going to be? Can you tell from looking up here at the grid?*

Children *It's right under the 4.*
It's the first one.
I know from the song—Sunday!
That's when I go to Sunday School, though.

Teacher *You're right. We won't be at school on Sunday. We'll have to wish Dan a happy birthday on Friday or Monday instead.*

. . . .

The Yearlong Paper Chain & A Link Each School Day

As February opens, children will count the links they collected in January and then add them to the yearlong chain in order to determine how many days they've been in kindergarten so far. This will provide yet another opportunity to begin anticipating the hundredth day of school.

Teacher *How many more links will we need to reach 100?*

Children *A lot!*
I don't think very many. 94 is already a lot.
It's really close—just 94—95, 96, 97, 98, 99, 100. It's only 6—I know 'cause I was holding up my fingers when I counted.

You'll also begin a new A Link Each School Day chain for February.

Our Month in School

This month, post a coin card that shows an enlarged penny for each day in school. At the end of each row of 5 pennies, you'll clip a nickel card to the side of the pocket chart to help children understand that a nickel is worth 5 pennies. These cards can also be used to help students learn to count by 5's. We suggest that you introduce these new cards by reading *Benny's Pennies*, an absolutely delightful book about a resourceful and kind little boy with 5 pennies to spend.

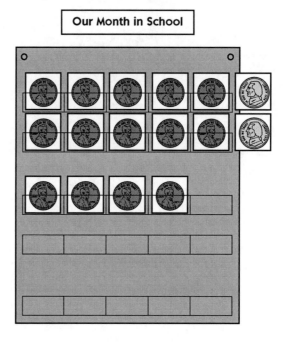

Yesterday, Today & Tomorrow

This month, you'll record significant classroom events under the Yesterday, Today, Tomorrow card. This will again provide many opportunities to use the language and grammar of past, present, and future. It will also give students a chance to reflect on past events and take a hand in planning future ones.

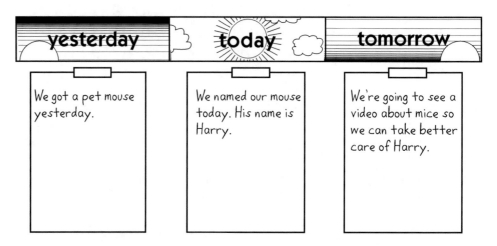

Day 100 Activities

The first activity in this collection of 4 involves a game of 20 questions in which children collect clues to identify a special treat you have hidden away —a bag of individually wrapped candies. In the second activity, students estimate how many candies are in the bag, count them onto ten-frames to find the actual number, and then work together to determine how many of the candies each child can have. In the course of the third activity, each child makes a crown decorated with 100 stars. In the fourth and final activity, each chef strings an edible necklace—100 cereal O's grouped into sets of 10. All four activities are designed to give children a better sense of that magical quantity—100. Even youngsters who aren't yet able to count by 10's will have the opportunity to count from 1 to 10 over and over in the course of these lessons, and if it's true that the stomach is one of the most powerful routes to learning, a few more of your children might emerge with the counting-by-10's sequence feeling a bit more comfortable. While all of these activities are definitely optional, we hope you'll enjoy including one, two, three, or even all four of them.

Notes

Day I

CALENDAR COMPONENTS

Introducing the February Daily Routines

On the first school day of February, children count the paper links they collected in January and add them to the yearlong chain. By now, the hundredth day of school will probably be drawing near—a big event in kindergarten. Students count to figure out how many school days remain until Day 100 and, after clearing the calendar grid of the January markers, post a special marker for this event in the appropriate pocket. Finally, the children work to create free-form collages in red, white, and blue for this month's calendar markers.

. . . .

Note If you have a favorite theme already planned for the month, adapt the instructions in this lesson so children can make calendar markers that will better fit your plans. Also, make a pattern strip to go along with your markers.

. . . .

. . . .

The Yearlong Paper Chain & A Link Each School Day

Skills

★ counting by I's

★ counting by I0's and I's

★ reading numbers above I0

★ counting on

You'll need

★ yearlong paper chain

★ the links you collected in January

★ I" × 7" construction paper strips (continue to use the same two colors)

★ scissors and glue

★ Paper Chain number labels for 80 and 90, with large paper clips attached

Gather children to the Number Corner. When all have arrived and settled, direct their attention to the paper chain links they collected in January.

A Link Each School Day

Day I Introducing the February Daily Routines (cont.)

How many 10's are displayed? Are there any additional 1's? How many links are there in all for the month of January? Count them one by one with the children and remove them from the calendar display. Then work with students to attach these links to the yearlong chain, cutting, gluing, and changing colors if necessary to form all the possible groups of 10. Finally, attach the extra 1's at the end of the chain. Next, have children help you stretch the chain out on the floor, and attach as many new number labels as necessary.

Then count the links by 10's, pointing to the labels as the children count with you. When you reach the 1's, point to each individual link carefully as you count them. Then ask children to count all of the links a second time, this time stretching their hands out to show 10 fingers for each group of 10 and clapping as they count the 1's.

Next, ask students how many days it will be until they've spent 100 days in school. Because 100 is a number of great power and magic to kindergartners, this may have come up in discussions last month. In any event, work with students now to determine how many more days it will be until Day 100.

Teacher I can't believe we've been in school 94 days, can you?

Children It's lots of days.
Our chain is really long—longer than our teacher.
I bet it's longer than my dad.

Teacher How many more links will we need to reach 100?

Children A lot!
I don't think very many, 94 is already a lot.
It's really close—just 94—95, 96, 97, 98, 99, 100. It's only 6—I know 'cause I was holding up my fingers when I counted.

Teacher 100 really is a large number, and a pretty special one too. Let's all try Kari's idea. She counted on from 94 until she reached 100, and held up 1 finger for each number she counted.

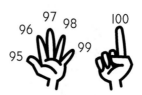

Once the class has determined how long it will be until Day 100, select a helper to construct the first paper link for February, and attach it to the A

Day I Introducing the February Daily Routines (cont.)

Link Each School Day label. As he works at this task, take a moment to point out that the new link represents another day in school. *Now* how many days until Day 100 (counting Day 100)?

> **Teacher** *If we added this link to our yearlong chain, how many links would we have in all?*

> **Children** *Lots!*
> *100!*
> *No, we had 94 before. This one will make it 95.*
> *Hey, now it's only 5 days until Day 100.*

. . . .

The Calendar Grid One Last Look at January

Skills

★ reading an ABC pattern

★ counting by I's to 3I

★ naming the days of the week

You'll need

★ Days of the Week song

★ completed January calendar grid

★ a 5″ × 5″ piece of construction paper in a bright color

★ the Day I00 marker

Before you remove the old markers from the grid, have the children read through last month's pattern as a helper points to each marker.

Then as a second helper points to the markers again, have students recite each of the counting numbers. Finally, sing the Days of the Week song for the entire month, quickly removing each of the markers from the grid as the days are named. When you get to the last marker, stop singing. What day *was* that? Slip a brightly colored square of construction paper into the pocket in the top row of the now-empty grid under the very next day to help everyone remember the starting point for posting the new markers, once they're made.

> **Teacher** *On which day did January end?*

Day 1 Introducing the February Daily Routines (cont.)

Children *Wednesday!*
This month starts on Thursday.
Put the paper in the Thursday pocket—the top one.

Teacher *Can someone tell me which pocket that is?*

Children *It's the one with T.*
Like Tommy—just find the one with his letter.

Teacher *Gosh, I'm a little confused. There are 2 days that start with T up here. Which one says Thursday?*

Children *The one at the end.*
Just sing the song and find it—here, I'll show you.
Thursday—it's not just the T one, the other one.
Sunday, Monday, Tuesday, Wednesday, Thursday—it's right there!

After you've marked the first day of February, work with children to find the right pocket for your special Day 100 calendar marker, using the information they got when they counted the links in the yearlong paper chain. If they discovered that there are 4 more days until Day 100, for instance, have them count that many *school days* on the calendar grid and place the Day 100 marker in the appropriate pocket.

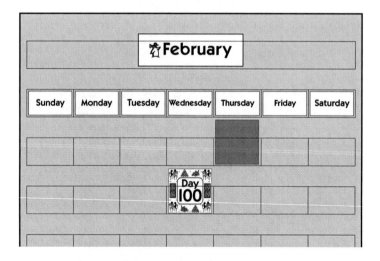

Children *Only 4 more days 'til Day 100!*
Are we going to have a party?
Is that the last day of school?
It's only 4 days until Day 100, but we left more empty boxes than that.

Teacher *We had to skip over Saturday and Sunday because we don't come to school on those days. It's 4 more school days until Day 100. We can't count the weekend days.*

Day 1 Introducing the February Daily Routines (cont.)

The Calendar Grid Making the New Markers

Skills

★ exploring the idea of 2-dimensional and 3-dimensional constructions

You'll need

★ 5" squares of construction paper in red, white, and blue. You'll need 28 squares for this month's pattern—7 reds, 14 whites, and 7 blues. If you only have one group, a few of the children may have to make an extra marker. If you teach double session kindergarten, it's probably safe to cut 20 of each color and let children choose which color they want.

★ ½" × 4" strips of construction paper in red, white, and blue. Cut enough for each child to have 10 to 12 strips, some in each color

★ glue

★ scissors

Now that the old markers have been removed from the calendar grid, it's time to make new ones. Explain to children that this month you're going to have them make miniature paper collages. Begin by taking a single 5" square of paper, a small handful of strips, a bottle of glue, and some scissors and, after writing your name on the back of the paper square, demonstrate a few techniques for creating such a collage. We like to show our children how to cut the strips to different lengths, trim or fringe them, accordion-fold them, wind them around a pencil to create paper curls, and glue them at intervals to create waves. This is a very open-ended project, and while some children will get plenty of joy out of cutting the strips to different lengths and gluing them to the paper, others will be thrilled to create collages that are more 3-dimensional. When you post these markers on the calendar grid through the month, the flat ones can be placed in the pockets as usual, while the more sculpted creations can be paper-clipped to the fronts of the pockets. Be sure to remind children to write their names on the back of their papers before they start gluing. Student interest in the calendar grid tends to remain higher if each child is acknowledged by name the day his or her marker is posted.

Note *To prepare these markers for tomorrow's session, you'll need to make sure you have 7 reds, 14 whites, and 7 blues. If you don't have enough of one color or another, you'll need to make some extras yourself or have students do so over the next day or two. If you have too many, you might send them home, use them to create an attractive mini-quilt for classroom display, or put them*

Day 1 Introducing the February Daily Routines (cont.)

out for children to sort and pattern during Work Places. You'll also need to decide, as you did last month, whether to glue the Calendar Numbers (Blacklines NC 2–NC 3) to the markers ahead of time or have students locate the needed numbers each day from a collection randomly displayed on your bulletin board or pocket chart. If you decide to glue the numbers to the markers ahead of time, be sure to sequence them in an ABBC (red, white, white, blue) sequence. Be sure, also, to include the Day 100 marker in the sequence, letting it take the place of a collaged square on the appropriate day.

. . . .

Day 2

CALENDAR COMPONENTS

Introducing the February Daily Routines

Now that the calendar markers are made, introduce the new pattern—ABBCABBC. Because this sequence is complex, we suggest that you take a few minutes to translate it into sounds and motions with your class. After children have clapped and snapped their way to becoming more familiar with this pattern, they help bring the calendar grid up to date, count the number of days left until Day 100, and post the new paper chain link. Finally, introduce a set of coin cards for the Our Month in School chart by reading *Benny's Pennies*, a wonderful book about money by Pat Brisson.

. . . .

The Calendar Grid Getting Started

Skills

★ reading and extending an ABBC pattern

★ translating a pattern from one form to another

You'll need

★ February pattern strip (If you're using markers to support a different theme, make a pattern strip to fit your markers.)

★ February markers children made yesterday

★ Calendar Numbers, sheets 1–2 (Blackline NC 2–NC 3, run 1 copy of each sheet for children to label the markers as you post them, or for your use)

Open today's session by inviting children to join you in the discussion area. Call their attention to the new pattern strip and read through the sequence of colors together. Then take a few minutes to explore this pattern by setting some sounds and motions to it.

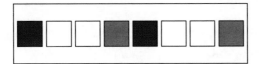

You might start with something relatively simple, perhaps having children tap their heads each time you point to the red square, clap on each of the whites, and slap their knees on the blue. As you point to each of the squares on the pattern strip, ask students to recite the color names as they tap, clap twice, and slap:

Day 2 Introducing the February Daily Routines (cont.)

"red, white, white, blue"

Have youngsters repeat this sequence—reciting the color names while performing these four actions—several times. Then ask them to stand and repeat the sequence several times again. Next, ask students to suggest a new motion for red, perhaps a jump, a quick squat, or a thumbs-up sign. Have the group repeat the sequence as you continue to point to the colors on the strip, substituting the new motion for the head tap. Then solicit suggestions for the two "white" moves, so the two claps become two stamps or maybe two waves. Next, call for a new blue move. By now the sequence of motions will be completely altered, but will still follow the ABBCABBC pattern.

"red, white, white, blue"

We find that young learners get a better feel for a pattern when they're encouraged to accompany the words with motions—sometimes the bigger, the better. You might also set the pattern to music, using three different tones, or have children build it with Unifix cubes. Speaking, seeing, hearing, moving, building—all of these help children continue to grow in their understanding that patterns repeat and for this reason are predictable.

After you've spent time with the pattern, have the children help you bring the calendar grid up to date.

> **Teacher** *Today is the second day of February. 2 days have passed. What color markers belong on our grid?*

> **Children** *We need a red for the first one.*
> *It should go where that paper is—the one that shows where to start.*
> *It's on the Th day—Thursday.*

Day 2 Introducing the February Daily Routines (cont.)

Teacher *Okay! What comes next, and what number should it be?*

Children *A white comes next! Red, white, white, blue; red, white.*
It's a white 2.
I hope it's mine—I made a white one and I put curls on it.
I made a blue one with lots of stripes.

Finally, ask children to figure out how many days remain until Day 100.

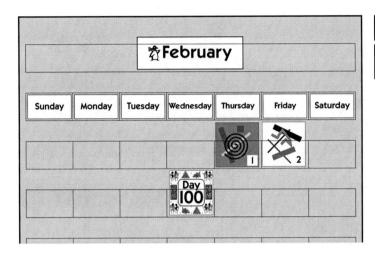

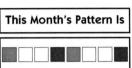

Children *It's 1, 2, 3, 4, 5 days until Day 100.*
I hope we have a big party.
Can we have a cake?
Let's have balloons, like on the picture.
5 days isn't so much.

- -

A Link Each School Day How Many Days Have We Been in School This Month?

Skills

★ counting by 1's

★ counting by 10's

★ adding "1 more"

You'll need

★ the 1" × 7" paper strips

★ glue

Next, direct students' attention to the A Link Each School Day display. How many school days have passed in February so far? Select a helper to construct a new paper link for today.

Day 2 Introducing the February Daily Routines (cont.)

. . . .

Our Month in School Introducing the Coin Cards

Skills

★ understanding that people use money to buy things

★ counting by 1's

★ recognizing "1 more"

★ recognizing pennies and nickels by name and value

★ exploring the idea that 5 pennies can be traded for a nickel

You'll need

★ Coin cards

★ *Benny's Pennies* by Pat Brisson

Once today's link has been posted, show children the new cards for the Our Month in School chart. This is a set of 20 pennies and 4 nickels. After children have had a chance to look at the cards and identify the 2 coins, explain that they'll be posting a new penny each day they're in class this month. How many pennies need to go up today? How many more pennies will it take to fill the top row?

> *Children* We need 2 pennies, 'cause it's been 2 days this month.
> We have 2 links on our chain—now we need 2 pennies.
> 1,2—I can show it on my fingers.
> There are 3 empty boxes, I can just see.
> It'll take 3 more pennies and then the row will be full up.

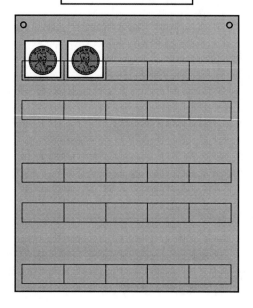

> *Teacher* How many pennies will we have when the top row is completely filled?

Day 2 Introducing the February Daily Routines (cont.)

> **Children** 1, 2, 3, 4, 5.
> It's 5 in the top row—I know that.
> 2 pennies and 3 more—that'll be 5.

Once children have had a chance to share some of their observations, tell them that each time a row is filled—each time there are 5 pennies—you'll clip a nickel to the chart at the end of that row, because a nickel is worth 5 pennies.

We suggest you conclude this session by reading *Benny's Pennies* by Pat Brisson. This is a delightful story about a young boy who has five new pennies and is given five different ideas about how to spend them. His mother advises him to look for something beautiful; his sister suggests something nice to wear. Benny's brother tells him to buy something good to eat, and his dog and cat second the motion. Clever Benny is able to fulfill all five requests and, in the process, gives a basic introduction to money and spending. Although some of your children may be experienced enough to know that pennies don't go very far in today's economy, they'll still be charmed by the story.

Day 3

 CALENDAR COMPONENTS

Introducing the February Daily Routines

It's the third school day of February, and the routines for the month are starting to fall into place. Today, children post the new marker and do some counting on the calendar grid to figure out when the 100th Day is coming up, as well as any birthdates anticipated this month. Then they attach a new link to the paper chain and put another penny card in the Our Month in School chart. Finally, introduce a new idea for the Yesterday, Today & Tomorrow routine. Instead of posting art projects or worksheets on the card, write a sentence or two under each heading to report three days' worth of class news several times during the month.

. . . .

The Calendar Grid What Comes Next?

Skills

★ reading and extending an ABBC pattern

★ determining duration on the calendar

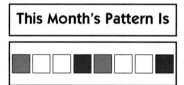

You'll need

★ calendar markers

★ February pattern strip

★ Calendar Numbers, unless you've already glued them to the calendar markers

★ February month heading and markers from your Here's When We Were Born chart (post these directly beside the calendar grid)

★ helper jar

To begin today's session, ask children to join you in the Number Corner. Once they're settled, draw their attention to the calendar grid and have them "read" the markers that have been posted as a helper points to each. Then ask them to make some predictions about today's marker. What color will it be? What number will it be? Under which day on the grid will it be posted?

> ***Children*** *Red, white, white, blue...*
> *Today has to be white!*
> *It's red—I know it's red 'cause that's how the pattern goes. Look up on that little paper. It goes red, white, white, blue; red, white, white, blue.*
> *I think it's going to be a blue. It goes white, white; now it'll be blue, blue.*
> *I don't know what it's going to be.*
> *Red, white, white, blue, red—it's red!*

Day 3 Introducing the February Daily Routines (cont.)

Once again, you may be surprised to find that your students vary significantly in their ability to extend this pattern. Some may understand the sequence quite well, and make predictions with great assurance. Others may be aware that the pattern is ABBCABBC, red, white, white, blue; red, white, white, blue, but find the sequence as it appears on the grid confusing. As long as the colors appear in a straight line, the pattern is clear to these students, but when the ABBC's of the pattern shift from row to row on the grid, their understanding may waver. You may still have a few youngsters for whom the entire concept of pattern continues to be a bit of a mystery, especially when the sequence is more complex than ABAB. These children may benefit from occasional opportunities during the month to move, sing, and dance the pattern; experiencing things on a kinesthetic level can be vitally important to some of your young learners.

> **Teacher** *Many of you are looking at the pattern strip to make your predictions, and seem fairly well convinced that today's marker will be red. Can you predict what the number on our marker will be as well?*

> **Children** *5—that's easy!*
> *It just goes 1, 2, 3, 4, 5. Today is number 5.*

> **Teacher** *Under what day of the week are we going to put this marker?*

> **Maxine** *Let's sing the song and find out. Can I point?*

> **Children** *Monday, Tuesday, Wednesday, Thursday, Friday, Saturday, and Sunday, the days of the week.*

Monday—it's Monday.

Once the marker for the day has been posted, ask children to figure out how many days remain until Day 100. If the day is drawing near, you may want to take a minute to discuss your plans: a party, special projects, all-school events, or other activities.

Day 3 Introducing the February Daily Routines (cont.)

Finally, call children's attention to the birthdate markers you've posted beside the calendar grid today. Explain that because they've become more experienced in reading a calendar, you're going to start moving the children's markers from the Here's When We Were Born chart onto the grid itself each month. Work with students to place one or two of the February markers on the grid in the appropriate pockets right now. (If you have more than a couple of birthdates this month, you'll want to spread this task out a bit, possibly returning to it several times today until all the markers have been posted.)

> *Teacher* Let's look at the February markers to see who was born in the month of February.

> *Children* I was! I'm going to be 6!
> I don't know when my birthday is.
> My brother has a birthday tomorrow.
> I went to my friend's birthday party on Saturday.

> *Teacher* Birthdays are really exciting, aren't they? Whose name is on the first birthdate marker in this collection?

> *Children* Suzy!
> I can tell 'cause of the s and the z.
> That's my card. My birthday is February 8th.
> Why did you move those little cards?

> *Teacher* I moved them because we're going to try something new this month. We're going to put the February birthdate markers on the calendar grid so we can see when each one is going to arrive. Suzy was born on the 8th of February. Can anyone see which pocket it belongs in on our grid?

> *Children* I know! Just count—it goes 1, 2, 3, 4, 5, 6, 7, 8. I'll show you!
> It's going to go right after that Day 100 card, I think.
> I wish my marker could be up there.

After they've had a minute to consider the problem, have a helper come up to the grid to point as the children count to determine where the first marker should be placed.

Day 3 Introducing the February Daily Routines (cont.)

Then move the marker itself to the grid and ask students to determine how many more days until this birthdate and on what day of the week it will occur. Each child who has a birthdate in February will want to be certain that he or she ends up featured on the grid today.

> **Children** *Suzy's birthday is under that day with Th.*
> *Thursday!*
> *It's really close—only 1, 2, 3 more days.*
> *It's right after Day 100.*

A Link Each School Day & Our Month in School

Skills

★ counting by 1's

★ recognizing pennies and nickels by name and value

★ exploring the idea that 5 pennies can be traded for a nickel

You'll need

★ the 1″ × 7″ paper strips

★ glue

★ Coin cards

★ helper jar

After a brief stretch and wiggle break, direct children's attention to the task of recording the number of days they've been in school this month. Select a helper to attach a new link to the paper chain for February. As she's working, have a second helper post another penny card. Then take a minute to discuss the Our Month in School chart. What do students notice? How many pennies have been posted so far? How many more will they need to collect in the chart before you can pin up a nickel? What about two nickels?

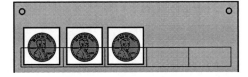

Our Month in School

Day 3 Introducing the February Daily Routines (cont.)

> **Children** *There are 3 pennies in the top row.*
> *We need 2 more to fill up that row.*
> *When we get 5, the teacher is going to put up a nickel, remember?*
> *1, 2, 3—it's not very much money.*
> *I wish we could buy stuff with 3 pennies like Benny.*
> *We could if those were dollars. We need dollars.*
> *If we get 7 more, we can get 2 nickels.*
> *If the whole thing was full, we'd have lots of nickels.*
> *That would be a lot of money.*

. . . .

Yesterday, Today & Tomorrow Class News Reports

Skills
★ Exploring the idea of yesterday, to-day, and tomorrow; past, present, and future

You'll need
★ Yesterday, Today, Tomorrow card

★ marking pen

★ paper, post I sheet under each heading

At the end of the Number Corner or, better yet, at the end of your kindergarten day, draw children's attention to the Yesterday, Today, Tomorrow card. Explain that this month, instead of posting art projects and worksheets, you're going to record class news. After a bit of discussion, work with children's help to compose two sentences—one that describes something exciting, unusual, or noteworthy that happened today, and one that describes an interesting event from yesterday. Use your marker to record these under the appropriate headings. Finally, compose a third sentence about tomorrow, based on something the children know is going to happen, or something you have planned and want to share with them ahead of time.

. . . .

Note *We suggest that you remove the Yesterday, Today, Tomorrow reports each day and start with a clean sheet of paper under each heading, rather than trying to move the events the way you shifted the papers and projects from heading to heading last month.*

. . . .

Day 4

CALENDAR COMPONENTS

Continuing Through February

By now, you've introduced all the daily routines for February, some new and some familiar. These include the new pattern on the calendar grid, the paper chain, the coin cards for the Our Month in School chart, and recording class news on the Yesterday, Today, Tomorrow card. Hopefully, these activities are going smoothly enough to be compressed into 10-minute lessons several days a week as you return to your regular math instruction. Here are some ideas to consider in shaping your Number Corner sessions over the rest of the month.

The Calendar Grid

• Once the February birthdate markers are posted on the grid, you can use them, along with the Day 100 card, to explore duration; how many days will it be until the hundredth day of school, or until the next birthdate?

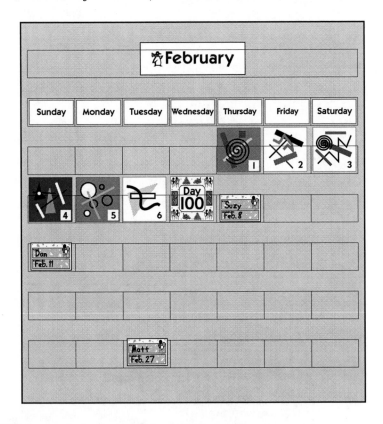

Children *Only 1 more day 'til Day 100.*
It's tomorrow! I hope we get 100 treats.
And then Suzy's birthday—only 2 more days.
It's a long time 'til Matt's birthday.

Day 4 Continuing Through February (cont.)

Teacher *What day of the week is Dan's birthday going to be? Can you tell from looking up here at the grid?*

Children *It's right under the 4.*
I know from the song—Sunday!
That's when I go to Sunday School, though.

Teacher *You're right. We won't be at school on Sunday. We'll have to wish Dan a happy birthday on Friday or Monday instead.*

• Continue to have children predict what the new calendar marker will be each day, using the pattern strip to help as necessary. On the days you don't have time to get to the Number Corner, have a helper post the calendar marker, the paper chain link, and the coin card.

• If you elected not to put the calendar numbers on ahead of time, you might display the rest of them, in random order on a nearby bulletin board, or even in the bottom few pockets of your calendar grid pocket chart. As the calendar marker goes up each day, have a helper locate the number that needs to be attached.

• Continue to model how to read the day and date every so often:
Today is _____, February _____, _____. Be sure to point to the day name, the month, the marker number, and the year label as you chant the date.

• Have children practice writing the numerals for the day's date in the air, on the rug, on individual white boards or chalkboards, or on the Numeral Writing Practice pages (Blacklines NC 6–NC 15).

• At the very end of the month, ask students to help you remove the even numbered markers from the grid and look at the pattern that remains. (You might use the Odd/Even cards from last month to help determine which numbers should be removed and which should stay posted.)

Day 4 Continuing Through February (cont.)

Children *All the blue ones are gone.*
Lots of diagonals
It looks like red stairs and white stairs.
It goes red, white, red, white, red, white.
It's a pattern!
It goes marker, skip, marker, skip, marker, skip.

Teacher *Let's try reading the numbers on the markers that are left.*

Children *1, 3, 5, 7, 9—all the odd numbers.*

. . . .

The Kid Count

Although we didn't include the Kid Count in the first three lessons for February, you might want to revisit this routine, in any of the versions listed below, every few days throughout the month.

• A very short version of this activity is simply to have children clap and count around the circle to determine how many students there are in class.

• The Number Rock is a hit with most kindergartners, and many of your students will surely want to repeat this version of the Kid Count several times this month. One variation, once they're lined up with their number cards and ready to sing, is to have them sit down when their numbers are sung. As soon as they're all down, rewind the tape, play it again, and have them stand up as they sing the song a second time.

• If you want to devote more time to the activity, have children count and clap around the circle and find the number on the Kid Count chart. You might use a red overhead marker to circle the number on the chart that shows how many students are normally enrolled in your class, and use it as a reference point in helping youngsters figure out how many are absent on any given day.

• On the days that you hand out the Kid Count cards and have children line up holding their cards in order, you might also ask them to set their cards on the floor and step away from them, if space permits. Then turn four or five of the cards face down while students close their eyes. Can they figure out which numbers are hidden?

. . . .

A Link Each School Day How Many Days Have We Been in School This Month?

• Continue asking a helper to add a link to the chain each day. When ten links are in place, change colors and start the second group of ten.

Day 4 Continuing Through February (cont.)

• Once or twice this month, you might have the children determine the total number of days they've been in kindergarten, counting the links on the year-long chain by 10's and 1's, or even by 1's if you have time, and then "counting on" with the links you've posted for February so far.

. . . .

Our Month in School Coin Cards

• Continue adding a penny card to the Our Month in School chart each day. Every time you fill a row, clip a nickel card to the edge of the chart. Take time, periodically, to discuss the amount of money in the chart. You may want to guide children in counting the pennies by 1's, or counting the nickels and pennies by 5's and 1's. It's also interesting, on occasion, to ask students to discuss what they see on the chart without directing their observations.

Teacher *What do you notice about our chart today?*

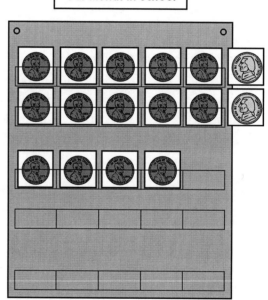

Children *We have 2 of those silver ones.*
Those are nickels. 5 and 5 is 10.
Lots of pennies. Not so many nickels.
Only 2 nickels. Way more pennies.
There are 14 pennies, I know.

Teacher *How did you know that so quickly?*

Ella *I just knew 5 in the top row and 5 in the next row—that's 10.*
And then 4 more goes 11, 12, 13, 14. It's 14 pennies.

Joshua *Can we count the pennies and the nickels together?*

Day 4 Continuing Through February (cont.)

Teacher *Sure. Those nickels are just clipped to the chart to remind us that 5 pennies are worth a nickel, but I don't see why we can't count all the money. How much would that be in all?*

Joshua *Well, 2 nickels—that's 10. Then 10 pennies on the top, so 10 and 10. That makes 20. Then 4 more is 24.*

Jorge *In another day, we'll get a new nickel. Then we'll have 3 of them.*

• Use the nickel cards to help children understand that 5 pennies are worth a nickel. Use these cards, also, to help students begin to learn to count by 5's. When you reach the end of the second row, and again when you reach the end of the third and the fourth row, take time to count the pennies by 1's. Then go back and count the nickels by 5's.

Teacher *We have 3 rows full now. Let's count the pennies together—ready?*

Children *1, 2, 3, 4, 5, 6, 7, 8, 9, 10, 11, 12, 13, 14, 15—15 pennies. I knew it already!*

Teacher *How did you know that without counting them?*

Julie *Every row has 5. I just know 5 and 5 is 10, and 5 more is 15. My mom showed me.*

Teacher *Wow! Let's go back and count the pennies 1 by 1. This time, though, I want you to stretch out 1 hand to show all 5 fingers each time we reach the end of a row. Ready?*

Children *1, 2, 3, 4, 5!*
6, 7, 8, 9, 10!
11, 12, 13, 14, 15!

Teacher *Good job! Now let's go back and count by 5's. I'll point to the nickels because they're each worth 5 pennies, and you stretch out one of your hands to show 5 fingers for each number. Here we go.*

Children *5, 10, 15!*

Day 4 Continuing Through February (cont.)

. . . .

Yesterday, Today & Tomorrow Class News Reports

Although you probably won't choose to use the Yesterday, Today, Tomorrow card more than once or twice a week, it's a good way to continue to teach the vocabulary and grammar of past, present, and future. You may find that a few of your students become quite excited about the idea of news reporting and come to you through the day with ideas for one or another of the headings on the card. The Yesterday, Today, Tomorrow card continues to provide an opportunity to do a bit of planning with your class about the next day, either alerting them to something you want them to be thinking about ahead of time, or possibly extending choices to them about the coming day's plans.

> **Teacher** *Let's report the news to go with our Yesterday, Today, Tomorrow card. What happened yesterday in class that's newsworthy?*
>
> **Children** *The gym was good. We got to play on the scooter boards. Yeah! And scoot really fast all around the gym.*
> *I almost crashed!*
>
> **Teacher** *Okay. It sounds like the gym was one of the best things about yesterday. What about today?*
>
> **Children** *That's easy! Today we had Day 100!*
> *We got a bag with 100 treats.*
> *When do we get to eat them?*
>
> **Teacher** *Well, you can have a choice. We can either make special hats tomorrow for Day 100, or we can figure out how many treats there are for each kid, divide them up, and eat them.*

> **Children** *Treats tomorrow!*
> *I want to make a hat.*
> *We can make hats the next day.*
> *There were 100 candies in that bag. I bet we can all have a bunch!*

Activity 1

DAY 100

What's in the Bag? 100 Wrapped Candies

Overview

The first hundredth day activity begins with an especially tantalizing opener— a large and mysterious sealed bag. The children will get to be detectives, asking questions to try to figure out what's in the bag. Once they've gathered 15 or more clues, and determined that candy (and perhaps even what kind) is inside, you'll open the sack to reveal the special treat.

. . . .

Note There are many varieties of wrapped candies available, so search for something that appeals to you and has lots in each bag. (We prefer to avoid round candies that might get caught in the back of the throat.) You'll want to count exactly 100 candies into your mystery bag. Also, if you're planning to do all 4 days' worth of Day 100 activities, we encourage to you read ahead, gather your supplies all at once, and arrange to have parent or student helpers on hand the last two days if at all possible.

. . . .

You'll need

★ 100 wrapped candies sealed in a large grocery bag

★ chart paper and marking pens

★ helper jar

Skills

★ asking questions to gather clues

★ observing and describing

★ estimating using a benchmark of 10

★ counting by 1's and 10's

Begin today's investigation by gathering children to your discussion area. When everyone is settled and can see the chart paper you've posted, show children the mystery bag. What do they think could be in the bag?

Encourage your students to discuss the possibilities with one another and then show them that you've stacked 15 Unifix cubes in 3 groups of 5, each group a different color, to help keep track of how many questions they've asked. Explain that they'll need to ask you questions that you can answer yes or no to find out what's in the bag.

Activity I What's in the Bag? (cont.)

Teacher *I'll remove a cube for each question you ask until you've gathered 15 clues. Let's see if you can collect enough information to figure out what's in this bag in just 15 questions. Who has a question that I can answer yes or no?*

Joshua *Do we get to eat it?*

Teacher *Yes.*

Marty *Is it good for us?*

Teacher *No, it tastes good but it's not very healthy to eat.*

Amy *It's doughnuts. I love doughnuts and my mom says I can only have them once in awhile 'cause they're not good for me.*

Teacher *How could you find out if it's doughnuts?*

Amy *You could just tell us.*

Teacher *You need to ask a question that will help you figure out for yourselves if there are doughnuts in the bag. Talk it over. What could you ask me that would help you find out?*

Jonny *Doughnuts are round. Is it round?*

Teacher *No, it's not round.*

Ella *Is it a rectangle?*

Teacher *There are some rectangles in my bag.*

Record the information they've gathered so far on your chart. How many questions have they asked? How many questions do they have left?

What's in the bag?

Yes	No
can eat it	not good for you
rectangle ☐	not round ⊗

Ella *My daddy likes those kind of doughnuts that are rectangles with that frosting on the top. It could be a doughnut even if it's not round. Is it one of those rectangle doughnuts?*

Teacher *I like those too, but it's not a doughnut, not even a rectangular doughnut.*

Activity 1 What's in the Bag? (cont.)

Kari *Do you have lots of stuff in there so we can all have one?*

Teacher *I do have lots.*

Matt *Is it sweet like candy?*

Teacher *It is sweet.*

Taylor *Is it candy?*

Teacher *It is candy.*

Children *Open the bag. Taylor figured it out. I'm hungry. Me too! How much candy do you have?*

Teacher *Taylor did figure out that it's candy, but let's take a look at our chart and see what else you've learned so far. Maybe you can find out what kind of candy is inside.*

Read over the chart together. What kind of candy could it be? How many Unifix cubes are left? Can they figure out seven more questions to ask?

Dan *Is there enough for everybody?*

Teacher *There is plenty.*

Continue in this way until the children have gathered 15 clues. If your class isn't close to figuring out what's in the bag at that time, offer them 5 more questions and provide a clue or two to get them on track. Finally, open the bag and show children the candy.

Activity I What's in the Bag? (cont.)

Teacher I think you've figured it out all right. Let's pour them out to see if your questions helped you gather accurate information.

Children We did it! Those are good.
I want the red ones.
I want the yellow ones.
When do we get to eat them?
I bet there are 100 in there.
Maybe it's thirty-ten!
Maybe it's a thousand!

Promise that you'll keep the candy in a safe place and give them a chance to count it tomorrow. Then they can figure out how many each child gets to eat.

Activity 2

DAY 100

How Many Candies?

Overview
Today, you'll gather children into the discussion circle to determine how many candies are really in the bag and figure out how many each child will get to eat.

Skills
★ estimating with a benchmark of 10

★ counting by 1's, 5's and 10's

★ counting on

★ exploring division

You'll need
★ the candies

★ Counting Mats (Blackline NC 57, run 10 copies on cardstock)

★ helper jar

Open the session by inviting children to join you in the discussion area. Pour out the candies and set out the counting mats. How many mats do they think the candies might fill?

Some children will make the connection to the hundredth day and be quite certain there are 100. How many mats would that take? Invite helpers (by pulling sticks from the jar) to fill three mats with candy. Once three mats are filled, have students count the candies that are already on the mats. How many do they have so far? How many more mats would they have to fill if there are really 100 candies?

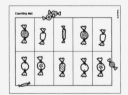 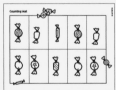 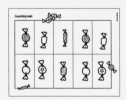

Teacher How many candies have we counted onto the mats so far?

Sammy It's 30. You just have to go 10, 20, 30.

Tommy You can do it by 5's too, though. 5, 10, 15, 20, 25, 30. It's like with the pennies and nickels on the chart.

Amy Let's do it the real way.

Many children won't trust the quantity to really be 30 without a chance to count it all by 1's. Taking the time to do so may help them begin to trust other counting patterns over time.

Activity 2 How Many Candies? (cont.)

> *Teacher* *How many more mats would we have to fill to have 40 candies?*

> *Joshua* *One more mat. You just keep counting after the 30. You could just know if you look up at our chain and those numbers. See, it's 30, then 40 next and there are 10 of those paper circles in there.*

Ask helpers to count out 10 more candies and count the assembled mats by 10's, 5's, and 1's. How many more candies would be needed to have 50? 100?

> *Teacher* *Let's get our helpers to keep filling these mats until all the candies have been placed. See if you can figure out how many we have as we go along.*

Once children have counted the candy several ways and trust that there are 100 pieces, get them up for a wiggle. Then pose the next problem: how many candies can each child have if you use up all 100 pieces and divide them up fairly? After you've explained the problem, give them a minute to speculate, and then ask for suggestions about how to proceed. How might they go about finding the answer?

> *Teacher* *This candy is for all of you. How many pieces do you think would be fair for each child in our class can have?*

> *Children* *2! No, maybe 5. Maybe 4. We have 24 kids so maybe it will be 3. I think it's going to be 10 for us. Does the teacher get any?*

> *Teacher* *You can have all the candies, but we need to be fair. How can you figure it out?*

> *Leslie* *Let's just give everybody 1 and then see if there are any left.*

Activity 2 How Many Candies? (cont.)

Sammy *But there are lots more candies than 1 each. Look! There are 20 right here and then these 4, so there are lots left. I think it's 3 or maybe 4 each.*

Ligia *We could do 2 each and then see.*

Dan *But there would be lots left over. It has to be 3 or 4.*

Randy *It might be 5 because maybe some people don't like candy.*

Teacher *If someone doesn't like candy, he or she can give it away. How shall we begin?*

Follow your students' suggestions to determine how to share the candy, but be certain they understand that they don't get to eat of the candy until the final determination is made about how to share fairly. If you have chocolate, have them set the candies on the back of a chalkboard or a piece of paper so they won't melt in hands while this enormous problem is being solved.

It's possible that they'll decide to settle for three each and then suggest that you take the rest home to your family or give them to the principal. We've seen that happen more than once in these kinds of activities. We've found it best to settle for the solution that seems to feel right to them.

Activity 3

DAY 100

The Hundredth Day Crown

Overview

The hundredth day crown consists of 100 stars arranged in strips of 10 to commemorate this special time in the kindergarten year. Though it will take some friendly, patient adult assistance to attach the strips together at the top in crown fashion, it will be worth the trouble when children wear their star crowns out the door looking like kings and queens during this week of celebration.

Skills

★ following directions

★ counting by 1's and 10's

★ reading the multiples of 10 to 100

You'll need

★ Hundredth Day: crown star strips (Blackline NC 37, run 2 copies for each student)

★ Hundredth Day: crown number band (Blackline NC 38, run 1 copy for each student)

★ scissors and glue for each students

★ a stapler or glue for the adults to use after the strips are glued to the band and dried

Open today's special Day 100 lesson by seating children in a circle in your discussion area. When they're settled, show children the papers with the strips of stars they'll be using to create a special hundredth day crown. How many stars are on each strip? How many stars are on one page? How many stars are on two pages?

Demonstrate how to cut each of the strips apart and set each of them safely in a stack so they won't get mixed up with another child's stack.

Then show students the crown number band and ask them to help you read each of the numbers. Explain that you want to cut these strips apart and then glue them together so that the numbers will be in one long line and will read 10, 20, 30, 40, 50, 60, and so forth, all the way to 100, just like the numbers that are hanging on the yearlong paper chain. Point out the cutting lines and the two glue tabs on the sheet.

Then cut the strips apart and demonstrate how to glue them together in a long line so that the counting by 10's numbers are in proper sequence.

Activity 3 The Hundredth Day Crown (cont.)

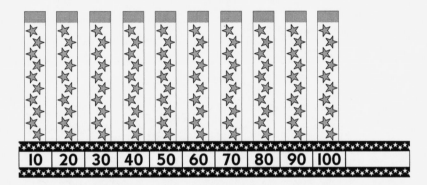

Next, show children how the strip will fit around their heads with some adjustment at the end and then model gluing each strip of ten stars in the center of a number box, at the back of the headband so the numbers aren't hidden. Write your name at the end of the head band strip and tell children that it will be very important for them to do this as well. When they're finished gluing, they'll need to put their crown in a designated place to dry. (This way you won't send them out the door with glue in their hair and running down their faces. We write from experience, and it's not a pretty memory.) Be sure their names are on them before they're set aside.

Once the work has dried, fit each headband to its owner's head and staple or glue it together. Then take two strips that are directly opposite one another and glue or staple them together. Pull up two more strips that are opposite one another and attach them. Continue this pairing and attaching at the top until all the strips are pulled into the center and the child's crown is complete. (This would be a great time to have some parent helpers or older students on hand, and would make a wonderful buddy class project if you were able to gather extra staplers.)

. . . .

Note *If you're planning to do the necklace project tomorrow (see Activity 4), you might want to have your students leave their crown at school overnight. The combined effect of the crown and the necklace is pretty splashy.*

. . . .

Activity 4

DAY 100

A Necklace of 100 Cereal O's

Overview

Though this final activity takes some preparation time and another outlay of money, it's a lot of fun and another way for children to deal with counting by 1's and 10's. If you have already done the candy activities, you may want to save this for another year and another group, particularly if your day always seems too short. If you decide to plunge in, you'll want to model all of the steps and then send children out to work. Be sure you do this on a day that your classroom will be vacuumed. If the cereal is sweet, you'll also want to wipe the tables at the end of the day—they're sure to be sticky.

Skills

★ counting by 1's to 10

★ counting by 10's to 100

You'll need

★ a large box of cereal that's shaped in O's that preferably come in more than 1 color

★ Hundredth Day: cereal O's necklace mat (Blackline NC 39, run a class set)

★ a blank piece of newsprint or copy paper for each student

★ a cotton string for each student approximately 36" in length

★ a small paper cup for each child partially filled with cereal

String Preparation

The day before this project, you'll want to cut the lengths of string and dip an inch or so at one end of each string into white glue and hang it to dry. This makes it work like a needle to push through the center of the cereal O's. Tie a Unifix cube on the other end to block the O's as they're strung on the necklace. (The cube will be cut off after the necklaces are finished and tied.)

Paper Cups for Cereal

Fill the individual cups about $1/3$ to $1/2$ full of cereal depending upon the size cup you're using. You can add more as needed. You'll probably run into some problems as children change colors with alternating 10's, and the last group of 10 or so may need to be a variety of colors.

Making the Necklaces

Be sure to have your children wash their hands before you begin this activity. Model the entire process by first showing children the project supplies: the cups of cereal, the prepared strings, the counting sheets, and the extra pieces

Activity 4 A Necklace of 100 Cereal O's (cont.)

of paper. Explain that the Unifix cube that's tied on the end is there to keep their cereal O's from falling off, but it will be cut off and returned to the Unifix cube tub after the 100 O's have been strung and the necklace has been tied. Pour out your cup of cereal onto a sheet of blank paper. Quickly sort the O's by color and then count 10 onto each of your ten-frames.

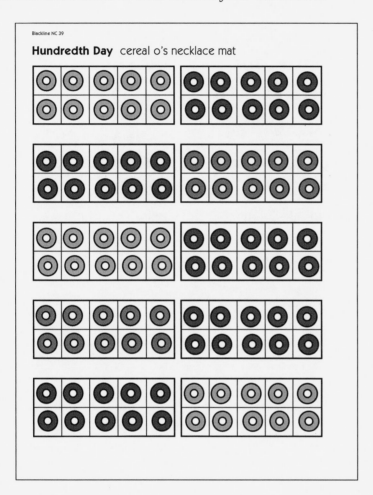

Demonstrate how to string each O over the glued end of the string, 10 at a time, changing colors with each group of 10 so it's easy to keep track of how many O's are on the necklace. Depending upon the needs and patience of your group, you may be able to stop your demonstration after you've strung 20 or so onto your necklace and simply talk them through the rest of the process.

Some children won't be able to resist nibbling as they string and will end up with fewer than 100 pieces on their necklace. Others may not have the patience to finish getting all 100 on the the string. Don't despair. They've once again had experiences with counting objects one by one and making groups of 10, as well as working happily side by side.

As they finish stringing their O's, have children sit where they are and raise their hands to get help tying the ends. (From experience we can tell you that

Day 4 A Necklace of 100 Cereal O's (cont.)

it's best not to have them walking around the room with untied strings of cereal. This is another great time to have a few extra pairs of hands around.)

When the necklaces are tied and ready to eat, have students don their necklaces so they can nibble throughout the day, or save the necklaces (and crowns if you didn't send them home after Activity 3) for them to wear out the door at the end of the day.

march

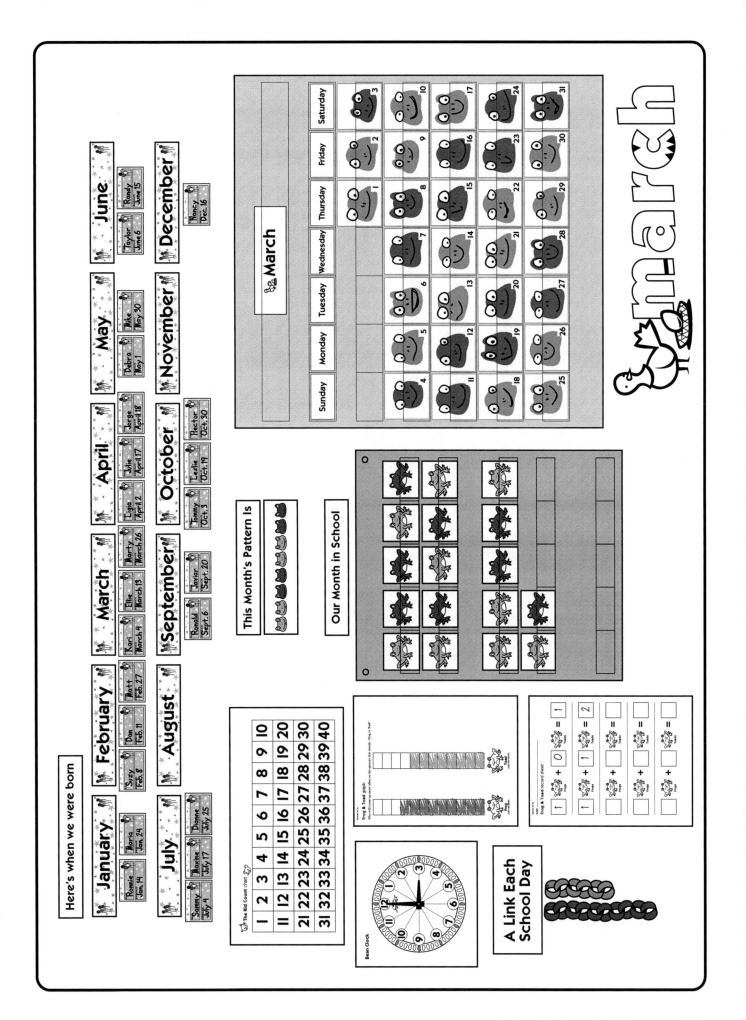

Introduction

It's March and, believe it or not, spring is right around the corner. In hopes of nudging things along, we've chosen frogs and toads as a theme for both the month's calendar markers and the Our Month in School chart. You'll find that many of the Number Corner routines take a leap forward this month as you help children begin to think about time, count higher than 100, develop their own pattern for the calendar markers, and launch into some interesting discussions about probability and data collection.

Shifting the Number Corner display from February into March and learning the new routines will take all of your math time for the first four days this month. Once the daily routines have been established, you'll be able to ease back into shorter Number Corner sessions and return to your regular math instruction.

The Calendar Grid

Although it's still a bit early for the peepers and croakers to make an appearance, we suggest that you move into the new month by reading Arnold Lobel's *Frog and Toad All Year* and then having your students make simple frog- and toad-face calendar markers. These are easily made by cutting and gluing construction paper and are guaranteed to perk up your Number Corner.

We're also suggesting that you jump-start spring by having students make up the pattern for the month rather than setting it for them. This involves a second day's worth of instruction in which you pose the problem, have children generate as many different patterns as they can with their frogs and toads, and then choose one to use on the calendar grid. You'll find the March pattern strip in the blacklines this month, ready to run on cardstock and to be colored according to the pattern your students choose.

Sammy *We could go toad, frog, toad, frog, like this.*

Maria *I know! We could do the other way—frog, then toad, then frog, then toad.*

Joshua *I have a good idea. How 'bout frog, toad, toad, frog, toad, toad?*

The Yearlong Paper Chain

As March opens, children will count the links they collected in February and add enough of them to the yearlong chain to bring the total to 100. Any that are left over will be used to start a second section of the yearlong chain, partly to keep the length of the first manageable—100 links is long enough!—and partly to help students develop a sense of 100 as 10 groups of 10.

Our Month in School Probability With Frogs & Toads

Frogs and toads serve as a springboard for a completely new activity on the Our Month in School chart this month. Using the Frog & Toad spinner and a set of Frog & Toad cards the children color, you'll begin a month-long probability experiment during the first few days of March.

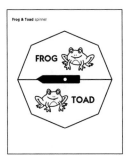

The question to be investigated is, what will happen if we spin the arrow on the Frog & Toad spinner every school day of the month? Is the arrow any more likely to land on the frog than the toad, or do they both have an equal chance? As adults, we know that the theoretical probability that the arrow will land on one amphibian or the other is equal—fifty/fifty. We also know that ten or even twenty spins aren't likely to produce equal results.

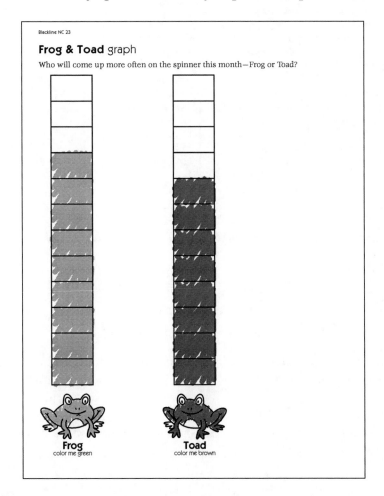

Kindergartners, being the magical thinkers they are, will likely predict that one or the other of the two creatures will "win" based on their personal preferences or wishes. This experiment will be repeated in April with two different characters, and is designed to provide children the opportunity to collect, record, and think about data generated by an experiment in which the outcome is partly determined by the initial setup. Will they understand that the frog and the toad are equally likely to be spun each day? Probably not, although some may comment that the spinner seems pretty fair. Over the period of a month, they will have a chance to observe that, in general, neither animal seems to win too many times before the other catches up, and that most likely the final totals don't differ by a huge amount.

. . . .

The Bean Clock

This month, you'll move into a more specific consideration of time by talking with the children about some of the things they do in the morning, the afternoon, and the evening, and recording their responses on a three-part chart. This chart will become part of your Number Corner display, along with a bean clock, which you'll post above the appropriate chart heading as you move the hands ahead by an hour each day.

Morning	Afternoon	Night
We wake up	We eat lunch	We have supper
We get dressed	- sandwiches	- spaghetti
We eat breakfast	- soup	- chicken
- cereal	- hamburgers	- rice
- toast with jelly	- carrots and apples	- tacos and beans
- tortillas	We play	We watch TV
- noodles	- ride bikes	We hear a story
We play with pets	- soccer	We brush our teeth
We watch TV	- basketball	We go to bed
We go to school	- computer	
	We watch TV	

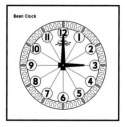

Teacher *Where is the short little hour hand on our clock today?*

Children *On the 3.*
That's in the afternoon—I can tell because I see a picture of a bike up there, and that's what we do after school.
I can tell it's in the afternoon, 'cause it's in the middle part of that paper.

Teacher *You're right. The clock says 3:00. In many schools, that's about the time the big kids get out of classes.*

This is the first in a series of activities you'll introduce between now and the end of the year to help your kindergartners begin to develop a sense of time, how people use a clock to measure time, and how to read a clock face to the hour.

Day 1

 CALENDAR COMPONENTS

Introducing the March Daily Routines

To open the month of March, children count the paper links they collected in February and add them to the yearlong chain. (We suggest that you use enough of last month's links to bring the total to 100, and then begin working on a second section of the yearlong chain to hang below the first. This is partly to keep the length manageable—100 links is long enough!— and partly to help students develop a sense of 100 as 10 groups of 10.) Next, the children take a final look at the February calendar grid, reciting the pattern, counting the markers, and working to determine when the last day of the month occurred. Finally, they create new calendar markers for March—paper frog and toad faces.

· ·

Note If you have a theme already planned for the month, feel free to adapt the instructions in this lesson so children can make calendar markers that will better fit your plans. Be sure to make a pattern strip to go along with your markers.

· ·

· ·

The Yearlong Paper Chain & A Link Each School Day

Skills

★ counting by 1's

★ counting by 10's to 100

★ reading numbers above 10

★ counting on from 100

You'll need

★ yearlong paper chain

★ the links you collected in February

★ 1" × 7" construction paper strips (continue to use the same 2 colors)

★ scissors and glue

★ Paper Chain number labels for 100 and 110, with large paper clips attached

Open today's session by gathering children to the Number Corner. When they've all arrived and settled, direct their attention to the paper chain links they collected in February.

How many 10's are displayed? Are there any additional 1's? How many links are there in all for the month of February? Count them one by one with the children and remove them from the calendar display. Then have students count how many links there are in the yearlong chain and use enough of the February links to bring the total to 100.

Day 1 Introducing the March Daily Routines (cont.)

Teacher *Our yearlong paper chain is getting very, very long. I'd like to add enough of the links we collected in February to bring the total to 100 and then start a new section. Let's count by 10's and 1's to determine the number of links in our yearlong chain so far, and then see if we can figure out how many more we'll need to add to bring the total to 100.*

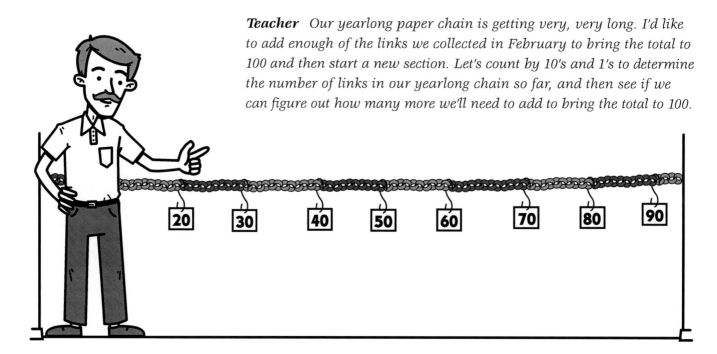

Children *10, 20, 30, 40, 50, 60, 70, 80, 90, 91, 92, 93, 94.*
There are 94 on the long chain.
It's almost 100.

Sammy *We just need* (whispers and counts on his fingers 95, 96, 97, 98, 99, 100) *6 more.*

Teacher *Let's all count on with Sammy to see if we agree that the yearlong chain needs 6 more links to reach a total of 100.*

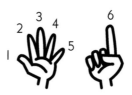

Children *Yep—it's 6 all right.*
You can see it on my fingers—it's going to be 6.

Once you've determined how many more links are needed to bring the yearlong chain to a total of 100, work with children to cut and move links from the February collection. Then have students help you stretch out the chain of 100 along the floor and set the remaining February links below this chain. Label the groups of 10 as necessary, and then count the links by 10's with children, pointing to the labels as you go. When you reach the 1's, point to each individual link carefully as you count them. Then ask children to count all of the links a second time, this time stretching their hands out to show 10 fingers for each group of 10 and clapping as they count the 1's.

Day I Introducing the March Daily Routines (cont.)

> *Children* It's more than 100.
> It's 113!
>
> *Teacher* We've been in school for 113 days—that's amazing, don't you
> think?

Once the class has determined how many days they've been in school so far
this year, select a helper to construct the first paper link for March, and attach it to the A Link Each School Day label.

. . . .

The Calendar Grid One Last Look at February

Skills

★ reading an ABBC pattern

★ counting by I's to 28

★ naming the days of the week

You'll need

★ Days of the Week song

★ completed February calendar grid

★ a 5" × 5" piece of construction paper in a bright color

Before you remove the old markers from the grid, have the children read
through last month's pattern as a helper points to each marker.

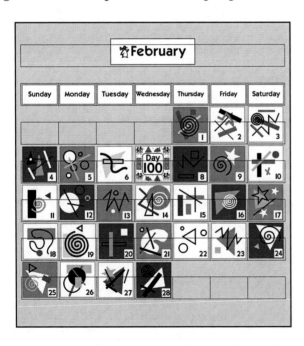
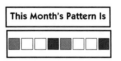

Then as a second helper points to the markers again, have students recite
each of the counting numbers. Finally, sing the Days of the Week song for
the entire month, quickly removing each of the markers from the grid as the
days are named. When you get to the last marker, stop singing. What day *was*
that? Slip a brightly colored square of construction paper into the pocket in
the top row of the now-empty grid under the very next day to help everyone
remember the starting point for posting the new markers, once they're made.

Day 1 Introducing the March Daily Routines (cont.)

. . . .

The Calendar Grid Making the New Markers

Skills

★ recognizing and naming squares and rectangles

★ estimating size

You'll need

★ 6″ × 8″ pieces of construction paper in green and brown (Cut 20 to 30 of each color, depending on the size of your class(es), and let each child choose the color he or she wants.)

★ 2″ squares of white and black construction paper (each student will need 2 of each color)

★ 5″ × 5″ white or yellow construction paper squares on which to mount the frogs and toads (optional)

★ glue

★ scissors

★ black crayons

★ *Frog and Toad All Year* or one of the other Frog and Toad books by Arnold Lobel

In honor of the coming of spring we suggest that you have your students make simple frog and toad faces for the March calendar markers. One of the ways to introduce this theme to your kindergartners is to read one or more of the stories from *Frog and Toad All Year*, or one of the other Frog and Toad books by Arnold Lobel. There are four books from which to choose—*Frog and Toad All Year, Frog and Toad are Friends, Days with Frog and Toad*, and *Frog and Toad Together*—and within these four books, more than sixteen short stories, any one of which would serve as a nice springboard for making the markers. If you're familiar with this collection of stories, you probably have your own favorites, and if the books are new to you, welcome to the world of Frog and Toad!

After reading one of these little stories and probably taking a minute to stretch and wiggle, have the children sit in a circle where they can easily see what you're doing. Draw a simple bean-shaped outline on one of the paper rectangles—green to make a frog or brown for a toad—and cut it out. The idea is to trim away enough paper so that the finished creation will fit into one of the calendar grid pockets, while keeping the marker large enough to be seen easily from across the room. Then show children how to use the white and black squares to cut circular eyes and eyeballs, and glue them to the head. Finally, add a smile and any other finishing touches, and write your name on the back.

Day 1 Introducing the March Daily Routines (cont.)

Teacher *I'm going to choose Toad for my calendar marker because he makes me laugh. I'll need a brown rectangle for his head, 2 white squares for his eyes, and 2 black squares to make his eyeballs. You'll need the same materials to make Frog, but you'll start with a green rectangle instead of a brown one.*

Teacher *First I'm going to draw the outline of Toad's head and cut it out. I'm going to try to make the head big—almost as big as my paper so people will be able to see it when it's up on the calendar grid.*

Then I'm going to cut big white circles for the eyes and smaller black circles for the eyeballs from my squares of paper.

Next, I'll glue the circles together like this, and then I'll glue them to the top of Toad's head.

Last, I'm going to take my black crayon and draw a big smile on Toad's face so that he looks as friendly as the character in our story. I want to put my name on the back, too, so everyone knows it's my marker when we put it up on the calendar grid this month.

Once children have watched you go through the process of making one of these markers, have them choose green or brown paper and head out to work. Don't worry if more students choose to make frogs than toads or vice versa. You will need some of each kind of marker—31 in all, or more—but the actual totals don't matter for now. You may want to have the other supplies—squares of black and white paper, scissors, black crayons, and glue—at their tables already. In addition, you may want to mount the frogs and toads on to yellow or white 5″ × 5″ squares.

. . . .

Note *Because children will figure out how to create a pattern with their frogs and toads tomorrow, there's really nothing more you need to do to prepare the markers. If you teach a double session, you'll have more than enough markers to work with already. If you only have one group, some of the children will have to make extra markers in the next day or two, but you'll probably want to wait until they've decided what the pattern is going to be so that you know exactly how many extra of each color you'll need.*

. . . .

Day 2

CALENDAR COMPONENTS

Introducing the March Daily Routines

Today, children work with their frog and toad markers to create a pattern for the calendar grid. They also examine a spinner that's used to determine whether a frog or a toad is posted in the Our Month in School chart each day. After considering the relative probability of spinning one or the other of the two animals, students help prepare the Frog & Toad cards for use during the rest of the month.

. . . .

The Calendar Grid Choosing a Pattern for the Month

Skills

★ creating and extending a variety of patterns

You'll need

★ March pattern strip (Blackline NC 21, run a single copy on cardstock, but don't color it until after children have determined the pattern.)

★ March markers children made yesterday

★ green and brown Unifix cubes

★ a yardstick or meter stick

★ Calendar Numbers sheets 1–2 (Blackline NC 2–NC 3, run 1 copy of each for children to label the markers as you post them, or for you to use)

Open today's session by inviting children to join you in the discussion area. Call their attention to the new pattern strip and ask them to share any observations they may have. It will be very interesting to see if anyone notices that the faces aren't yet colored, and that it's virtually impossible to distinguish the frogs from the toads, or discern any pattern at all on the strip.

Teacher Here's the new pattern strip for the month. What do you think?

Children It looks like the frog things we made yesterday.
There are a bunch in a row—1, 2, 3, 4, 5, 6, 7, 8.
My toad I made looks like those guys, except he's brown.
Which ones are the frogs? I can't tell.

Teacher Why not?

Hector It should be green for frogs and brown for toads. Can we color them in?

Day 2 Introducing the March Daily Routines (cont.)

>*Teacher* Sure—good idea. Which ones should be green and which ones brown?
>
>*Maria* Easy—green, brown, green, brown. Just make it in a pattern.
>
>*Teacher* Is that the only pattern we could make?
>
>*Sarah* You could go green, green, brown, like that.

Once children have had a chance to comment on the strip, explain that the reason it's not colored in is because you wanted them to make up the pattern this month. Set out the frog and toad markers they made yesterday and invite them to think of some patterns that could be made with the two different colors. As they discuss the problem, have pairs of students lay six to eight of the markers out in the middle of the circle to illustrate each new idea. Use your yardstick as a guide so the lines of markers are relatively straight and distinct from one another. Ideally, you'll have enough markers to leave each pattern out on the floor as new ones are proposed. If you begin to run short of markers, though, you might want to record some of the patterns with brown and green Unifix cubes so children can keep track of all the different proposals.

>*Sammy* We could go toad, frog, toad, frog, like this.

>*Ligia* Green is my best. Can we have green, green, brown, green, green, brown?

>*Teacher* What a lot of different ideas you've invented. Can anyone think of any different ways to pattern these markers?
>
>*Julie* I have a good one! We could make it go green, green, brown, brown—like this!

After students have come up with several different ideas, work with the class to choose one of the proposed patterns. If you teach double-session kindergarten, you might give one group or the other the final say about the pattern for the month.

Day 2 Introducing the March Daily Routines (cont.)

Youngsters will have an opportunity to create the pattern again next month with a different set of markers, so perhaps your afternoon group can make the final decision this month, and the morning group can do so next month.

Once the pattern has been chosen, explain that there are 31 days in March, and that you'll need to work together to see if there are enough frogs and toads in the collection to keep the pattern going for all 31 days. If there aren't enough of one or both kinds of markers, make arrangements with some of your students to create more some time in the next day or two. You or one of your students will also need to color in the pattern strip to match the sequence the class has selected. Decide, too, whether you want to glue numbers to the frogs and toads ahead of time or have children help you do so as the markers are posted on the grid each day.

. . . .

A Link Each School Day How Many Days Have We Been in School This Month?

Skills
★ counting by 1's
★ counting by 10's
★ adding "1 more"

You'll need
★ 1" × 7" paper strips
★ glue

After they've had a chance to explore some different patterns and select one for the calendar markers, take time for a little wiggle, and then direct students' attention to the A Link Each School Day display. How many school days have passed in March so far? Select a helper to construct a new paper link for today.

Day 2 Introducing the March Daily Routines (cont.)

. . . .

Our Month in School Setting the Stage for a Probability Experiment

Skills

★ exploring probability

★ recording data

You'll need

★ Frog & Toad cards (Blackline NC 22, run copies on cardstock and cut the cards apart along the heavy lines. You'll need at least I for each student to color, and 30 or more cards in total.)

★ Frog & Toad spinner

★ a chalkboard, chalk and eraser, *or* white board, marker, and eraser for each student

★ green and brown crayons to share

Once today's link has been posted, explain to the children that you're going to use a special spinner this month to decide what kind of card to put in the Our Month in School chart each day. Show them your Frog & Toad spinner and ask them to share any observations they may have. Be sure students notice that half the spinner belongs to the frog, and half belongs to the toad. Which animal, if either, do they think might come up more frequently if you were to make ten spins? Encourage children to share their reasoning as they make predictions, and don't be too surprised if the fact that the spinner is equally divided between the two animals has little influence on their thinking.

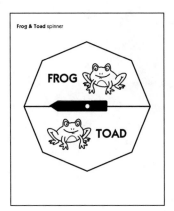

Teacher This month, we have a spinner to help us decide what kind of card to put up on the Our Month in School chart each day. What do you notice about this spinner?

Children It's got a frog and a toad on it!
They're like the ones on the pattern strip.

Day 2 Introducing the March Daily Routines (cont.)

I love that green guy—he's my best.
Toad's more funny in the story, though. He does such silly stuff.

Teacher *How much of the spinner belongs to each of these characters?*

Joshua *It's split in half. They each get half. That's what my mom*
makes me do when I get a cookie. I have to give half to my little sister.

Teacher *I think it's great that you share things with your sister,*
Joshua. Frog and Toad are each happy that they get half of this spinner,
too. What do you think will happen if we spin the arrow 10 times? Do
you think the arrow will land on one or the other of them more often?

Children *I want the frog to win—he's green, my best color.*
I think Toad will win because he's bigger than Frog in the story.
Frog's taller, though.
But Toad's fatter. He eats more cookies, remember?
Maybe the arrow could land on both of them the same 'cause they each
have half. That would be the most fair.

After students have had a chance to make some predictions, have them each
collect a set of writing materials (board, marker, and eraser) and rejoin you in
the circle. Tell them that you're going to spin the arrow 10 times, and that
you want each of them to keep score on their board.

This will mean that they'll have to figure out some way to show how many
times the arrow lands on the frog, and how many times it lands on the toad.
If you want a chance to observe children's organizational skills, and can stand
the fact that some of them won't know what to do, or will come up with
methods that don't make much sense to you, don't give them any more instruction than this. It's truly fascinating to watch what they do, and they can
certainly be encouraged to look at one another's boards to get ideas.

Day 2 Introducing the March Daily Routines (cont.)

When everyone is ready (more or less), spin the arrow 10 times while they keep score. Then discuss the results. Although the theoretical probability is fifty-fifty, it is possible that in the course of 10 spins, one or the other of the two animals will wind up with more than half. Even if the final score is 6 to 4, this will be taken as a true triumph by the children rather than a close game. And if, by chance, the score does turn out to 5 to 5, many students will still be convinced that one or the other of the animals will have a better chance of winning in the future. In any case, promise the children that you'll spin the spinner every day to see if the frog or the toad comes up, and keep score by placing a card for that animal in the Our Month in School chart, as well as by marking a graph. By the end of the month, each of the animals will have had plenty of chances to win.

Conclude today's session by having children help prepare the Frog & Toad cards. You'll need 15 to be colored green and 15 to be colored brown. If you have two sessions, this shouldn't be any problem and any extra cards might be used for decorations or simply spirited away. If you only have one group, however, you'll need to handle this in a more scientific manner.

Day 3

 CALENDAR COMPONENTS

Introducing the March Daily Routines

Today, children bring the calendar grid up to date. They also work with you to post the March birthdate markers on the grid and attach a new link to the paper chain. Finally, they insert the first three cards on the Our Month in School chart, spinning each time to see whether it's a frog or toad, and tracking the results on a graph as well as on a new record sheet.

. . . .

The Calendar Grid Getting Started

Skills

★ reading and extending a pattern

★ locating information on a calendar grid

★ determining duration on the calendar

You'll need

★ calendar markers

★ March pattern strip, colored in to match the pattern your class developed yesterday

★ Calendar Numbers, unless you've already glued them to your calendar markers

★ March month heading and markers from your Here's When We Were Born chart (post these directly beside the calendar grid)

★ helper jar

Invite children to join you in front of the Number Corner display. Show them the pattern strip for the month, colored in to match the pattern they chose yesterday. (We've colored in the strip below in an AABB pattern—green, green, brown, brown—but your class may choose something different.)

Which animal, the frog or the toad, will be posted first on the calendar grid, and where? It's the third school day of the month, but it may be the 4th or 5th of March, depending on the day of the week the month began. With children's help, figure out how many markers need to be displayed to bring the calendar grid up to date. If you haven't already glued numbers to the markers, the students will also need to help you with this task.

Day 3 Introducing the March Daily Routines (cont)

Once the calendar grid has been updated, draw children's attention to the March birthdate markers. Who was born this month? Have students read the names and numbers on the cards, and work with them to place one or two of the markers on the grid. This task provides wonderful opportunities to help children understand the structure of the calendar grid, especially if you ask them to try to figure out where the markers should be placed and what day of the week each birthdate is going to occur. If you have more than a couple of birthdates this month, you'll might spread this job out over the day.

> **Teacher** Let's see whose birthday is coming up in March.

> **Kari** Mine just went past. I had my party on the weekend. I'm 6 now.

> **Teacher** What number do you see on Kari's marker here?

> **Children** That's easy—it's a 4.
> Today is number 5, so Kari's birthday is over now.

> **Teacher** You're right about that. Whose name is on the next card?

> **Ellie** That's my name. My dad told me my birthday is coming real soon.

> **Teacher** Can anyone figure out where Ellie's birthday belongs on our grid? Where should we put her marker?

> **Children** It says 13.
> I know! Start on the number 1 frog and keep counting—1, 2, 3, 4, 5, 6, 7, 8, 9, 10, 11, 12, 13.
> You can just count from the 5 frog too—6, 7, 8, 9, 10, 11, 12, 13.

> **Teacher** Let's move Ellie's marker into that pocket right now. There we go. What day of the week will it be when her birthday comes along?

Day 3 Introducing the March Daily Routines (cont)

Ligia If we sing the Days of the Week Song, we can find out.

Tommy It's Tuesday, I know 'cause I looked up in the top row and I can just see it's the day that starts with a T, like my name. Tommy—Tuesday.

A Link Each School Day & Our Month in School
Introducing Probability with Frog & Toad

Skills

★ counting by 1's

★ exploring probability

★ using a graph to record data

★ exploring the use of standard notation to record addition combinations

You'll need

★ 1" × 7" paper strips

★ glue

★ Frog & Toad cards children colored yesterday (You'll need 15 of each, green frogs and brown toads)

★ Frog & Toad spinner

★ Frog & Toad graph (Blackline NC 23, run 1 copy and post it alongside the Our Month in School chart)

★ Frog & Toad record sheet (Blackline NC 24, run a copy and post it alongside the Our Month in School chart)

★ a green crayon and a brown crayon

★ helper jar

After a brief stretch and wiggle break, direct children's attention to the task of recording the number of days they've been in school this month. Select a helper to quickly attach a new link to the paper chain for March. As he's working, explain that you're going to have some helpers spin the Frog & Toad spinner to see which cards should be posted for the first three days of school this month. Based on yesterday's experience, what do the children think will happen?

Day 3 Introducing the March Daily Routines (cont)

Teacher *Here's our Frog & Toad spinner. We're going to spin the arrow 3 times today, because we've been in school 3 days already in March. We need to start getting our Frog & Toad cards placed on the chart. What do you think will happen if we make 3 spins today?*

Children *I think we'll get the frog 3 times because he's the best.*
Toads are stronger. I think they'll win today.
Frogs won yesterday, though—remember? We got 6 frogs and only 4 toads. I bet we'll get more frogs.
The arrow's pointing to a frog right now. If you push it really hard, it'll come back to the frog.
I can't tell what will happen. It could be the frog or the toad.

Teacher *What do you mean, Jorge?*

Jorge *They both have the same on the spinner. Half for the frog and half for the toad.*

Mike *I think frogs are better. The frog will probably win.*

After a bit of speculation, choose a helper to spin the arrow and then post the appropriate card in the first pocket. Discuss the results with students and color in the graph to show what happened. Then write a number sentence at the top of the record sheet to show how many frogs and how many toads there are on the chart at this point.

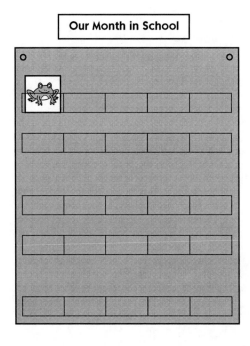

Our Month in School

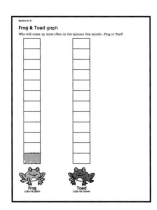

Frog & Toad graph
Who will come up more often on the spinner this month—Frog or Toad?

Frog
color me green

Toad
color me brown

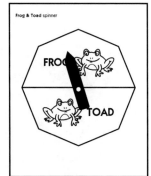

Frog & Toad spinner

FROG

TOAD

Day 3 Introducing the March Daily Routines (cont)

Teacher *So, the first time around, the spinner landed on the frog. Sarah put a frog card in the first pocket, and I colored the first box above the frog on the graph to show the results. Now I'd like to write a number sentence to show how many frogs and toads we have up here so far.*

Children *But there aren't any toads yet.*
Just 1 frog.
I knew frogs were going to win.
Toads are too bumpy—that's why the arrow can't land on them.

Teacher *It's true that we don't have any toads on our chart yet. So what numbers should I write on our record sheet for the frogs and the toads?*

Children *1 and none—0 for the toads.*
1 plus 0—that's just 1.

Repeat the process twice more—spinning, placing the designated card in the chart, coloring the graph, and writing number sentences to show the results. As you work with the children to do these tasks, you might continue to engage them in discussion about the likelihood of spinning one animal or the other. You'll also want to talk about how the results of the spins are being recorded in three different ways—by placing cards on the chart, coloring the graph, and writing addition sentences.

Teacher *Our third spin turned out to be a frog, and Maxine put the card in the chart for us. I colored in the graph. What number sentence will I have to write on our record sheet now? Our first sentence was 1 + 0 because we had 1 frog and 0 toads on the chart. Then we spun a toad and had to write 1 + 1. What should we write this time?*

Leslie *It has to be 2 and 1. We have 2 frogs and 1 toad.*

Joshua *Write 2 + 1. That makes 3, I know.*

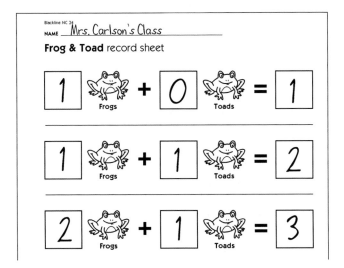

Day 4

 CALENDAR COMPONENTS

Introducing the March Daily Routines

The March markers are made, the pattern established, the calendar grid brought up to date. The paper chain has grown to three links and you've introduced a new way to use the Our Month in School chart that combines probability, data collection, and basic operations. On the last day before returning to your regular math instruction, talk with children about time—morning, noon, and night—and share a fourth routine for the month of March: the Bean Clock.

. . . .

The Calendar Grid What Comes Next?

Skills

★ reading and extending patterns

★ learning the days of the week

★ determining duration on the calendar

You'll need

★ calendar markers

★ March pattern strip

★ Calendar Numbers, unless you've already glued them to your markers

★ helper jar

To begin today's session, ask children to join you in the Number Corner. Once they're settled, draw their attention to the calendar grid and have them "read" the markers that have been posted as a helper points to each. Then ask them to make some predictions about today's marker. What color will it be? What number will it be? Under which day on the grid will it be posted?

Children Frog, frog, toad, toad, frog...
Today has to a be frog!
It goes 2 frogs, then 2 toads, then 2 frogs.
Yep! It's a green guy all right.

Day 4 Introducing the March Daily Routines (cont.)

Teacher *You're certainly doing a good job of using the pattern to make predictions about the marker for today. What number will it have on it?*

Children *It's going to have a 6 on it, 'cause 6 comes after 5.*
1 , 2, 3, 4, 5, 6.
I'm 6 now!
I'm going to be 6 this month.

Teacher *Under what day of the week are we going to put this marker?*

Maxine *Let's sing the song and find out. Can I point?*

Children *Monday, Tuesday, Wednesday, Thursday, Friday, Saturday and Sunday, the days of the week. Monday, Tuesday!*
It's Tuesday.
I know 'cause yesterday was Monday, and Tuesday always comes next.

Once the marker for the day has been posted, ask children to figure out how many days remain until the next birthday, and possibly the one after that if interest remains high.

. . . .

A Link Each School Day & Our Month in School

Skills

★ counting by 1's

★ counting by 10's

★ exploring probability

★ adding "1 more"

★ using a graph to record data

★ exploring the use of standard notation to record addition combinations

You'll need

★ 1" × 7" paper strips

★ glue

★ Frog & Toad cards

★ Frog & Toad spinner

★ Frog & Toad graph

★ Frog & Toad record sheet

★ a green crayon and a brown crayon

★ helper jar

Next, choose a helper to make the next link for the month's paper chain. As she's working, have children look at the number of frogs and toads they've collected on the Our Month in School chart so far this month. What do they think will happen with today's spin?

Children *3. We have 3 up there. Only 2 more to fill the row.*
It goes frog, toad, frog—it's a pattern!
Hey, I know! Today will be a toad for the pattern—frog, toad, frog, toad.
I think frog's going to win again today. Frogs can hop higher than toads.

Day 4 Introducing the March Daily Routines (cont.)

After they've had a chance to comment on the situation, choose a helper to make the spin for today and post the designated card in the fourth pocket on the chart. Record the results on the graph and then work with children to write an addition sentence that shows how many frogs and how many toads have been posted.

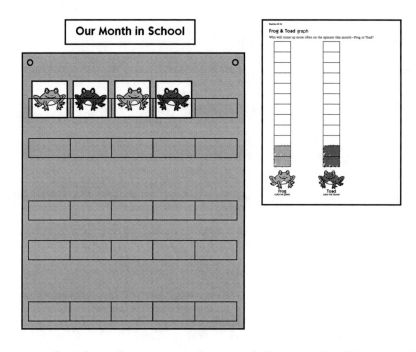

Deepak *It kept the pattern—frog, toad, frog, toad. It'll have to be frog tomorrow.*

Teacher *What number sentence should we write today? It will have to tell how many frogs and how many toads we have up here so far.*

Children *We have 4.*
We have 1 and 1 and 1 and 1.
There are 2 frogs and 2 toads.
2 and 2 is 4, you know?

Teacher *All of your observations are true. On our record sheet, though, there is only 1 box for the frogs and 1 for the toads, and then 1 box at the end to report the total. What one number can we use to describe how many frogs are on the chart?*

Ella *2! Just write 2 and 2 makes 4.*

After you've recorded a number sentence, work with children to read the sentence aloud and interpret the meaning of each number, in terms of the Frog & Toad cards.

Teacher *Let's read this sentence together. It goes like this: 2 plus 2 equals 4. People use that as a way to say that 2 and 2 is the same as 4.*

Day 4 Introducing the March Daily Routines (cont.)

What does the first 2 in this number sentence mean? Where can you see 2 on Our Month in School chart?

Children   *There are 2 frogs.*
You can also see the frog and toad together—they're friends. And then there's another frog and toad together.
2 frogs and 2 toads. It's 4.

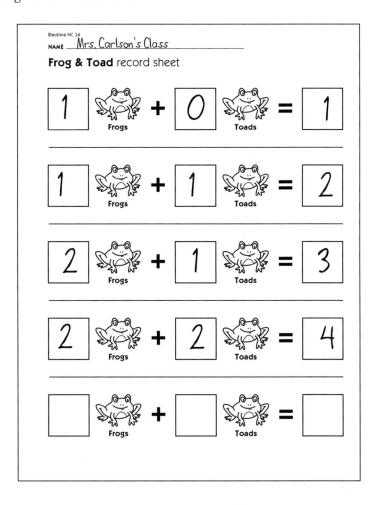

Day 4 Introducing the March Daily Routines (cont.)

· ·

The Bean Clock Introducing the Idea of Telling Time

Skills

★ exploring the idea of morning, noon, and night

★ exploring the idea that people use clocks to help keep track of the time

You'll need

★ the Bean Clock (Blackline NC 29, run I copy on cardstock, laminate, and attach hands.)

★ a piece of chart paper and a felt marker

Over the past two months, you've explored the idea of yesterday, today, and tomorrow. Take a few minutes now to talk about past, present, and future compressed to the scope of just one day—morning, afternoon, and night. Have children brainstorm a list of some of the things they do during these three time periods. As they talk, record some of their ideas on chart paper. If you can illustrate a few of them with quick sketches, so much the better. (Be sure to save this list—you'll need it for time-telling activities throughout the month.)

Teacher We're going to talk a bit about time today. Let's think about the morning time first. What are some of the things you do first thing in the morning?

Children I get up out of bed!
My mom wakes me up, but I'm always sleepy. I wish I could just stay in bed longer.
My kitty always wakes me up—she just licks my face.
Our baby cries and then I wake up.
I get dressed and help my little brothers.
We eat cereal and watch TV—my best cartoon is in the morning.

Day 4 Introducing the March Daily Routines (cont.)

Continue the discussion, moving on to afternoon and night. You can move through this fairly quickly—the topic will come up many times again over the next few months.

After children have generated a list of some of the things they do morning, noon, and night, ask them how they know what time it is. What tells them when it's morning, or noon, or night? How do they know when to get up, eat lunch, go to bed? How do they know when their favorite TV show is coming on? Since most of them can't yet tell time, encourage them to go a bit beyond the expected response of "Look at the clock." What do they do if they can't yet read a clock and there's no adult around to tell them what time it is? You may find their answers both fascinating and revealing.

> ***Children*** *I ask my big brother.*
> *I just watch what everyone else is doing.*
> *I can tell by the TV. I know which show is on right before it's time to catch the bus.*
> *I can tell time a little.*
> *I tell by when it's dark and light. I wake up right when it gets light, but my mom always makes me stay in bed. Sometimes I sneak out, though.*
> *I do too, and get my own cereal and watch TV with the sound real low.*
> *I can tell by when I get hungry.*
> *My computer tells the numbers of what time it is.*
> *We have a clock that tells the numbers too. I know when it's 6 and 3 and 0 that it's almost dinner time. My dad showed me how to do that.*
> *My cat always comes around and begs for food at dinner time.*

After some discussion, tell children that humans have lots of ways to tell when it's morning, afternoon, and night, but that many, many people all over the world use clocks of one sort or another to help them keep track of the time. Then explain that you have a new cardboard clock to post in the Number Corner. Show students that this clock doesn't really run, but that you can set the hands on it to various times, and that you're going to work together this spring to begin to learn to tell time. Pin your clock to the display board with a promise to return to it tomorrow.

Day 5

 CALENDAR COMPONENTS

Continuing Through March

By now, you've introduced all the daily routines for March, including the new pattern on the calendar grid, the paper chain, and the Frog & Toad spinner and cards for the Our Month in School chart. You'll be using the Bean Clock in a variety of ways from now until the end of the school year, but for the rest of March, work with your students on telling time to the nearest hour by moving the hands ahead one hour each day. Here are some other ideas to consider in shaping your Number Corner sessions this month.

The Calendar Grid

• Once the March birthdate markers have been posted, you can use them to explore the passage of time and to help children become more familiar with the structure of the grid itself. Here are some of the types of questions you might ask about the markers:

Whose birthdate is first this month? second? third?

How many days until the next birthdate?

On what day of the week will it be?

Whose birthdate is coming up in 8 days?

Who has a birthdate on a Monday this month?

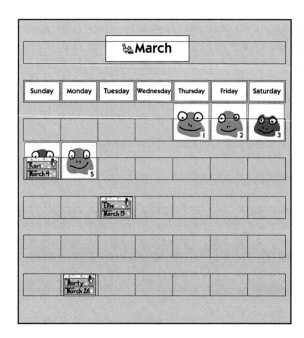
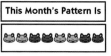

Day 5 Continuing Through March (cont.)

• Continue to have children predict what the new calendar marker will be each day, using the pattern strip to help as necessary. On the days you don't have time to get to the Number Corner, have a helper post the calendar marker and the paper chain link.

• If you elected not to put the calendar numbers on ahead of time, you might display the rest of them, in random order on a nearby bulletin board, or even in the bottom few pockets of your calendar grid pocket chart. As the calendar marker goes up each day, have a helper locate the number that needs to be attached.

• Continue to model how to read the day and date every so often:
Today is _____, March _____, _____.
Be sure to point to the day name, the month, the marker number, and the year label as you chant the date.

• Have children practice writing the numerals for the day's date in the air, on the rug, on individual white boards or chalkboards, or on the appropriate Numeral Writing Practice Pages (Blacklines NC 6–NC 15).

. . . .

A Link Each School Day How Many Days Have We Been in School This Month?

• Continue asking a helper to add a link to the chain each day. When ten links are in place, change colors and start the second group of ten.

• Once or twice this month, you might have the children determine the total number of days they've been in kindergarten, counting the links on the year-long chain by 10's and 1's, or even by 1's if you have time, and then "counting on" with the links you've posted for March so far.

. . . .

Our Month in School Exploring Probability With Frog & Toad

• Continue spinning the Frog & Toad spinner each day, and adding the designated card to the Our Month in School chart. Be sure to record the results of the daily spin on the Frog & Toad graph so children can see the information represented in two different ways. Take a few minutes every so often to discuss the cumulative results of this probability experiment. Is the arrow landing more often on the frog or the toad? Is either animal way ahead, or are they about even? How many times has the arrow landed on the frog? On the toad? How many more are there of one animal than the other so far?

Day 5 Continuing Through March (cont.)

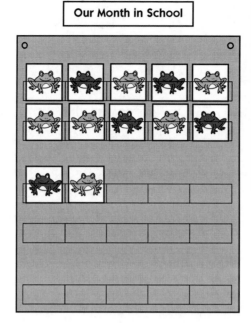
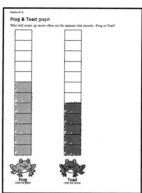

Our Month in School

Teacher *What do you notice about the frogs and toads on our chart?*

Children *We got 2 frogs in a row.*
There's a pattern up there. It goes frog, toad, frog, toad, frog in one row.
Frogs are more.

Teacher *How do you know?*

Sarah *I can count them. There are 1, 2, 3, 4, 5, 6, 7 frogs, and only 1, 2, 3, 4, 5 toads.*

Teacher *Is there any other way to tell that there are more frogs than toads so far?*

Sammy *Look at the color-in thing. The frog side is higher.*

Teacher *You mean the graph? How many boxes are colored in on the frog's side?*

Sammy *It's 7, just like the cards. You can see that it's more 'cause it's higher up.*

Teacher *How many more boxes would the toad need to catch up with the frog?*

Children *7!*
No, wait—it's not 7.
The toad already has some—he only needs 2 more to be up with the frog.

- You'll probably want to continue to write addition sentences to reflect the number of frogs and toads on the chart each day.

Day 5 Continuing Through March (cont.)

We have designed the record sheet to accommodate five number sentences, which makes it convenient to start all over again with each new row. In the case of the chart above, where a frog card has just been added to the second row, you could count all the frogs and toads spun so far and record 3 + 3 = 6 at the top of the second record sheet. You could also focus on the numbers in the second row alone, and record 1 + 0 = 1, working your way up to 5 again, and then starting once more with the third, and then the fourth row.

You might also choose to write number sentences for up to ten pockets at a time, starting over again as you start collecting cards in the third row. This will depend on the interests and capabilities of your students. The illustration below shows the record sheets from a class where the teacher elected to work with the frogs and toads as they were added to the chart over the first ten school days in March. She'll start over again from 1 when the 11th card is added.

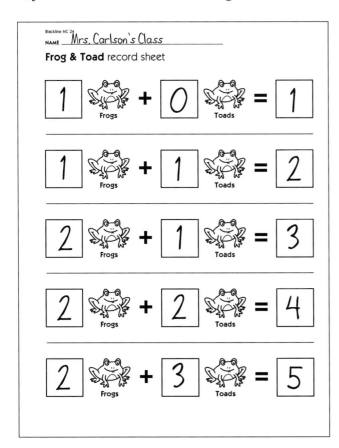

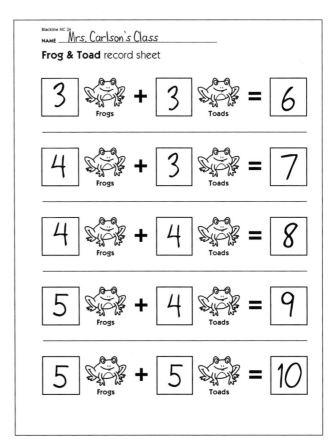

Day 5 Continuing Through March (cont.)

The Bean Clock Beginning to Tell Time to the Hour

- In order to familiarize children with the clock face and the idea of telling time to the hour, we suggest that you keep the bean clock on display in the Number Corner all month, and simply shift the hour hand ahead one hour each day. Make this time a meaningful one, like recess time, lunch time, etc. Discuss the time shown on the clock with your students in the most basic terms (i.e., "When the big hand is on the 12 and the little hand is on the 7, the time is 7 o'clock.")

In order to lend this activity a bit more meaning, you might hang the clock above the Morning, Noon, and Night chart children generated yesterday. To begin, set the hands at 7:00 and hang the clock above the morning heading. Explain to the children that it says 7 o'clock, an early morning time—perhaps the time when some of them get up on school days. Another day have the clock set to a different hour and relate it to something meaningful to the children. Shift the clock occasionally to hang over the afternoon or evening portion of the chart. Continue to relate the time it displays to events meaningful to the children.

Morning	Afternoon	Night
We wake up We get dressed We eat breakfast - cereal - toast with jelly - tortillas - noodles We play with pets We watch TV We go to school	We eat lunch -sandwiches -soup -hamburgers -carrots and apples We play - ride bikes - soccer - basketball - computer We watch TV	We have supper - spaghetti - chicken - rice - tacos and beans We watch TV We hear a story We brush our teeth We go to bed

Teacher *Where is the short little hour hand on our clock today?*

Children *On the 3.*
It's 3 o'clock.
That's in the afternoon—I can tell because it says "ride bikes" up there, and that's what we do after school.
I can tell it's in the afternoon, 'cause the middle part of that paper is afternoon stuff.

Teacher *You're right. The clock says 3:00, and that's an afternoon time. In many schools, that's about the time the big kids get out of classes.*

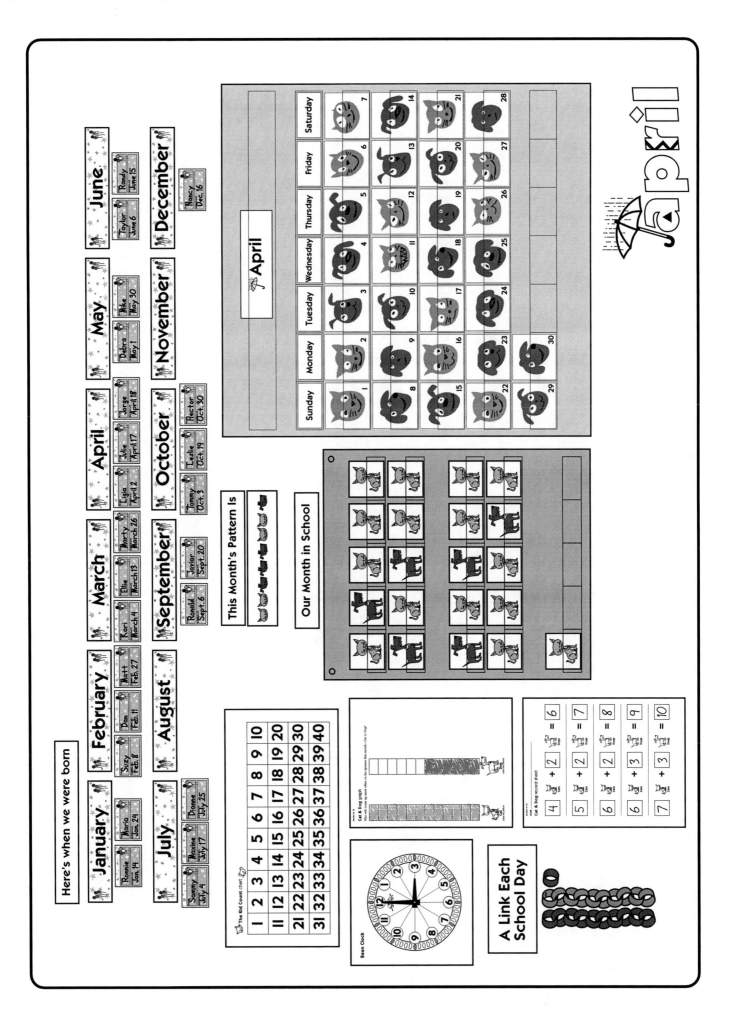

Introduction

This month, cute puppies and kittens scamper in to replace the frogs and toads of March, and if last month felt like a great leap forward in terms of the skills and concepts you introduced, April gives you a chance to consolidate some of the gains. This month, like last, children will work together to develop a pattern using the markers they've made. They'll conduct a second probability experiment, spinning a special spinner, posting the designated cards each day, and graphing the results. Students will also continue to work on telling time to the hour with the bean clock, a new set of clock cards, and a cute clock poem.

Shifting the Number Corner display from March into April and learning the new routines will take all of your math time for the first three days this month. Once the daily routines have been established, you should be able to ease back into shorter Number Corner sessions and return to your regular math instruction.

The Calendar Grid

There's something so perky and friendly about cats and dogs (or kittens and puppies, if you prefer) that it seemed like a perfect theme for the April calendar markers. Before your students make these simple cut-and-paste construction paper animal faces, you might want to read a favorite book about cats and dogs, or pets.

We also suggest that you let children again create the pattern for the month. This involves a second day's worth of instruction in which you pose the problem, have children generate as many different patterns as they can with their cats and dogs, and then choose one to use on the calendar grid. Things become even more interesting if children have made more dogs than cats (or vice versa) the day before. You'll find the April pattern strip in the blacklines this month, waiting to be run on cardstock and used for the pattern your students choose.

. . . .

The Yearlong Paper Chain

As April opens, children will count the links they collected in March and add them to the second section of the yearlong chain. The first section, 100 links long now, can be left hanging on display, in order to reinforce the idea that the first part of the year is over and done with, and the days in school are still accumulating. (We always have a few kindergartners who are astonished to find that the school year doesn't end on Day 100!)

. . . .

Our Month in School A New Probability Experiment

Cats and dogs serve as a springboard for a probability experiment that's similar to the one you conducted in March—with one little change. As you can see, the spinner isn't divided equally between the two animals this time. This is a deliberate move to challenge children's ideas about probability, many of which will still involve factors other than the structure of the spinner.

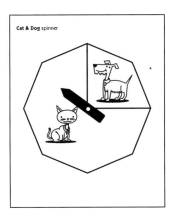

The question to be investigated is, what will happen if we spin the arrow on the spinner every school day of the month? Is it any more likely to land on the cat than the dog, or do they both have an equal chance? While you're not likely to see 20 spins produce 15 cats and 5 dogs, the cats are almost surely going to win by a fair amount this month.

Many of your kindergartners will probably make predictions about the results of this experiment based on their personal preferences or wishes. The fact that the spinner is heavily skewed to the cat will bear out, though. Despite the fact that many children may like the dog better, or figure that it will win because it is bigger, cuter, or stronger, youngsters will have the chance to observe that over a period of several weeks, the arrow is more likely to land on the cat.

The other change in this routine is that you will give students the opportunity to develop their own ways to represent the data from time to time. Last month, you modeled the use of standard addition sentences to record how many frogs and toads were posted on the Our Month in School chart. This month, you'll ask students to invent their own ways to show the data. Although a few may imitate your methods, you may be surprised and delighted to find that many of your students have other ways to represent what they see.

The Bean Clock

Assuming that you introduced the Bean Clock last month, you'll use a new set of clock face pocket chart cards to provide children with continued opportunities to practice telling time to the hour. The games that you'll play with your class involve matching these cards to times you set on the Bean Clock. After a few days of practice, you'll introduce a poem in which ten of the children will sit lined up in chairs holding the clock cards sequenced from 1 to 10. As you and the students recite the poem, they'll stand one by one, holding the cards for all to see. On the final line, they'll all sit back down to show that they've fallen asleep—snore!

Day I

CALENDAR COMPONENTS

Introducing the April Daily Routines

To open the month of April, students count the paper links they collected in March and add them to the yearlong chain. Next, the children take a final look at the March calendar grid by removing the odd numbers to look at the pattern that remains, and then removing the even numbers to determine when the last day of the month occurred. Finally, they make the new calendar markers for April—paper cat and dog faces, ready to frisk around and make spring in the Number Corner a little more fun.

. . . .

The Calendar Grid Painting Paper for the New Markers (optional)

Skills
★ art

You'll Need
★ tempera paint in cat colors (yellow, orange, brown)

★ tempera paint in dog colors (brown, grey, black)

★ 12″ × 18″ piece of white or manila construction paper for each student

If you want to make the calendar markers extra special this month, take a day before you do the Day 1 activities to have each student create a sheet of sponge-painted paper, as described in the paragraph below. After this hand-painted paper has dried, you'll cut it into 3″ × 3″ and 6″ × 6″ squares for children to use, along with small pieces of black and white construction paper, in making their cat or dog faces. (We don't worry about making sure that each child gets squares cut from the paper he or she painted—that's *too* much work!) Plan to have about half your students paint paper in cat colors, and half of them paint paper in dog colors.

To paint, pour a small amount of undiluted tempera paint in each of the cat colors (yellow, orange, and just a dab of brown) on a styrofoam tray. Pour dog colors (brown, grey, and a touch of black) on a second tray. Working with four to five students at a time and small pieces of kitchen sponge, show children how to dip their sponges into the colors.

Day 1 Introducing the April Daily Routines (cont.)

Caution them to keep a light touch as they paint, by dabbing their sponges instead of dragging them. They only need to renew the paint on their sponge every three or four dabs. Plan to replenish the paint frequently, because it does get mixed. We give each of our students a piece of paper on which to paint and encourage them to experiment with different effects. We let them choose whether they're going to paint their paper in dog colors or cat colors, but we keep the two trays well away from each other. You'll end up with quite a variety of painted papers, and most children will be very pleased with their efforts.

The Yearlong Paper Chain & A Link Each School Day

Skills

★ counting by 1's

★ counting by 10's to 100

★ reading numbers above 10

★ counting on from 100

You'll need

★ yearlong paper chain

★ the links you collected in March

★ 1" × 7" construction paper strips (continue to use the same two colors)

★ scissors and glue

★ Paper Chain number labels for 120 and 130, with large paper clips attached

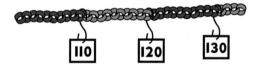

110   120   130

Gathering children to the Number Corner. When they've all arrived and settled, direct their attention to the paper chain links they collected in March.

How many 10's are displayed? Are there any additional 1's? How many links are there in all for the month of March? Count them one by one with the children and remove them from the calendar display. Then work with students to attach these links to the second section of the yearlong chain—there are already 100 in the first section, which you can leave hanging where it is for now. As in previous months, you might have to do a little cutting and gluing, and perhaps some color switching to create all the possible groups of 10 as you attach the new links to the second section of the yearlong chain.

Day I Introducing the April Daily Routines (cont.)

Label any new groups of 10 as necessary, and then count the links in both sections of the yearlong chain by 10's with children, pointing to the labels as you go. (If you want to be really dramatic about this, you might have the entire class move to the location in the room where the first section of 100 is hanging and stand to count as you point to each of the 10 groups of 10. Then have the children return to the rug and sit down to count the links in the second section—110, 120, 130—counting up over 100 can be quite exciting.) When you reach the 1's, if there are any in the second section of the yearlong chain, point to each individual link carefully as you count them. Then ask children to count the links in both sections of the chain a second time, stretching their hands out to show 10 fingers for each group of 10 and clapping as they count the 1's.

Once the class has determined how many days they've been in school so far this year, select a helper to construct the first paper link for April, and attach it to the A Link Each School Day label.

The Calendar Grid One Last Look at March

Skills
★ reviewing odd and even numbers
★ counting by 2's to 30
★ naming the days of the week

You'll need
★ Ten-Frame Odd & Even cards
★ Days of the Week song
★ completed March calendar grid
★ a 5″ × 5″ piece of construction paper in a bright color

Work with children to remove just the odd-numbered March markers from the grid. You may have to get out your Ten-Frame Odd & Even cards to help, but once children remember that 1, 3, and 5 are odd, many of them will notice that there's a pattern to the removal process itself. Take the first marker off, leave the second one on; take the third marker off, leave the fourth one on, and so on. When all the odd numbers have been removed, ask a helper to point to each of the remaining markers as the children read the pattern. It's frog, toad, frog, toad, or green, brown, green, brown on our grid, but may turn out to be something different on yours. Then have a second helper point

Day I Introducing the April Daily Routines (cont.)

to the markers again as students read the numbers that remain on the grid—
2, 4, 6, 8, 10, and so on—all the even numbers!

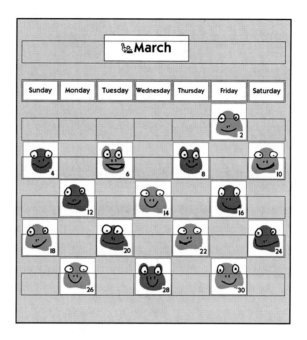

Finally, sing the Days of the Week Song and remove a marker each time its
day is mentioned. (In the case of the markers displayed below, the class
would sing, Monday, Tuesday, Wednesday, Thursday, Friday—the first
marker would come off—Saturday and Sunday—the second marker would
come off—the days of the week. Monday, Tuesday—another marker off—
Wednesday, Thursday—another marker off—and so on.)

When you get to the last marker, stop singing. What day *was* that? Since
March has 31 days, not 30, you'll have to slip a brightly colored square of construction paper into the top of the now-empty grid *two days* past the last
marker you removed. As in previous months, this marker will help everyone
remember the starting point for posting the new markers tomorrow.

Day 1 Introducing the April Daily Routines (cont.)

> *Teacher* *The last marker we removed from the grid was the one for Friday, March 30. March has 1 more day, though—an odd number so we can't see it up here. That means March ended on Saturday, and the new month starts the day after. What day comes after Saturday in our song?*
>
> *Children* *Sunday!*
> *Look! The new month starts exactly in the very first box this time.*

. . . .

The Calendar Grid Making the New Markers

Skills

★ recognizing and naming squares and rectangles

★ cutting triangles, ovals, and circles

You'll need

★ 6″ × 6″ squares of construction or hand-painted paper in yellow and brown. Cut 20 to 30 squares of each color, depending on the size of your class(es), and let each child choose the color he or she wants.

★ 3″ × 3″ squares of construction or hand-painted paper in yellow and brown (each student will need 2 of one color or the other)

★ 2″ × 2″ squares of white and black construction paper (each student will need 2 white and 3 black to make eyes and nose)

★ 5″ × 5″ white construction paper squares on which to mount cats and dogs

★ glue

★ scissors

★ black crayons

Cats and dogs (or kittens and puppies) scamper into the pockets of the calendar grid this month to keep the spring theme going. If you have a cute book about dogs and cats, or pets, perhaps, to introduce the new markers, read it now. If not, just dive right in. Most kindergartners seem to relate to dogs and cats easily, even if they don't have pets of their own at home.

To get started, draw a simple oval-shaped outline on one of the paper rectangles—yellow to make a cat and brown for a dog—and cut it out as the children watch. The idea is to trim away enough paper so that the finished creation will fit into one of the calendar grid pockets, while keeping the marker large enough to be seen easily from across the room. Then show students

Day 1 Introducing the April Daily Routines (cont.)

how to use the smaller squares of yellow or brown to make ears, one of the black squares to make a nose, and the white and black squares to cut circular eyes and eyeballs. We like to turn the oval sideways for the cat's face and lengthwise for the dog as we glue on the features, but you can fashion these markers any way that pleases you. Finally, add a smile and any other finishing touches, and write your name on the back.

> ***Teacher*** *I'm going to make both a cat and a dog, so you can get some ideas for how to make yours. While I'm working, think about which of the 2 you'd most like to make.*
>
> ***Teacher*** *First I'm going to draw the outline of a cat's head. I'll make it an oval shape and cut it out. I'm going to try to make the head big—almost as big as my paper so people will be able to see it when it's up on the calendar grid.*
> *Next, I'll use my 2 smaller squares of yellow paper to cut 2 triangle-shaped ears.*
> *Now I'll cut a little triangular nose.*
> *Then I'm going to cut 2 white circles for the eyes and smaller black circles for the eyeballs from my squares of paper. Next, I'll glue the circles together, like this.*

> *Last, I'm going to glue on the ears and the nose, and draw in a mouth and some whiskers. I want to put my name on the back, too, so that everyone knows it's my marker when we put it up on the calendar grid.*
>
> ***Teacher*** *For the dog's head, I'll start with an oval again. Next, I'll use my 2 smaller squares of brown paper to cut 2 long oval-shaped ears.*
> *Now I'll cut a nice round nose.*
> *I'll make the eyeballs the same way I made them for the cat.*
> *Next, I'll glue the circles together like this.*
> *Now I'll glue all the dog's features to his head—eyes, nose, and ears.*
> *Now I'll draw my dog's mouth—he's smiling. I'll put my name on the back, and now I'm finished!*

Once the children have watched you go through the process of making both the cat and the dog, have them choose yellow or brown paper and head out

Day 1 Introducing the April Daily Routines (cont.)

to work. Don't worry if more students choose to make dogs than cats or vice versa. You will need some of each kind of marker—30 in all, or more—but the actual totals don't matter for now. You may want to have the other supplies—squares of black and white paper, scissors, black crayons, and glue—at their tables already.

· ·

Note *Because children will figure out how to form the pattern with their dogs and cats tomorrow, there's really nothing more you need to do to prepare the markers. If you teach double session, you'll have more than enough markers to work with already. If you only have one group, some of the children will have to make extra markers in the next day or two, but you might want to wait until they've decided what the pattern is going to be so you know exactly how many extra of each animal you'll need.*

· ·

Day 2

 CALENDAR COMPONENTS

Introducing the April Daily Routines

Today, children work with their cat and dog markers to create a pattern for the calendar grid. They also examine the spinner that's going to be used to determine whether a cat or a dog is posted in the Our Month in School chart each day. This spinner, which allots three quarters of the circle to the cat and only one quarter to the dog is quite a bit different than the spinner the class used last month, and it's very interesting to see if it has any effect on children's predictions. After considering the relative probability of spinning one or the other of the two animals, students will help prepare the cat and dog cards for use the rest of the month.

. . . .

The Calendar Grid Choosing a Pattern for the Month

Skills

★ creating and extending a variety of patterns

You'll need

★ the March markers children made yesterday

★ yellow and brown Unifix cubes

★ yardstick or meter stick

★ April pattern strip (Blackline NC 25)

★ Calendar Numbers sheets 1–2 (Blacklines NC 2–NC 3, run 1 copy for children to label the markers as you post them, or for you to use)

Invite children to join you in the discussion area. Explain that this month you can't make a pattern strip at all until they've created a pattern with their markers. Then set out the dog and cat markers they made yesterday and invite them to consider some of the ways they might create a pattern with these animals. Before they start creating patterns, though, take a minute to have them count each of the collections. Because you let them choose which of the two they wanted to make yesterday, there may be more dogs than cats or vice versa. Once the children have counted to see how many markers are in each pile, encourage them to use this information as they discuss possible patterns.

>*Teacher* So, how many dogs do we have in our pile here?

>*Children* 23!
>*There are lots more dogs than cats.*

Day 2 Introducing the April Daily Routines (cont.)

Teacher *How many cats were there when we counted?*

Maxine *Only 8. That one on top is mine.*

Teacher *This makes our patterning problem really interesting. How can we make a pattern that uses lots of dogs and doesn't take so many cats?*

David *I know! Do dog, cat, dog, cat, dog, cat!*

Teacher *That would be a possibility, but we don't have very many cats.*

Children *We could make some more cats!*
Can I make another cat? I have 3 cats at home—they're my best pet!

Teacher *We don't have much time to make extra markers this month. Can you think of a pattern that wouldn't need so many cats?*

As they discuss the problem, have pairs of students layout 9 or 10 of the markers in the middle of the circle to illustrate each new idea. Use your yardstick as a guide so the lines of markers are relatively straight and distinct from one another. Ideally, you'll have enough markers to leave each pattern out on the floor as new ones are proposed. If you begin to run short of markers, though, you might want to record some of the patterns with yellow and brown Unifix cubes so children can keep track of all the different ideas.

Children *I have a good idea. How 'bout dog, dog, cat, dog, dog, cat. That'll use up more dogs.*
We could do the cats first, like this: cat, dog, dog, cat, dog, dog.
Let's go dog, dog, cat, cat, kind of like last month.
But that takes too many cats!

Day 2 Introducing the April Daily Routines (cont.)

Teacher *You're doing some great thinking here. Does anyone have another idea for a pattern that takes more dogs than cats, so we don't have to make lots of extra markers?*

Joshua *I have a really good one—cat, cat, dog, dog, dog, like this.*

After students have come up with several different ideas, work with the class to choose one of the proposed patterns. If you teach a double-session kindergarten, you might give one group or the other the final say about the pattern for the month. If your afternoon group decided on the pattern last month, perhaps the morning group could make the final choice this month.

Once the pattern has been chosen, explain that there are 30 days in April, and that you'll need to work together to see if there are enough cats and dogs in the collection to keep the pattern going for all 30 days. If there aren't enough of one or both kinds of markers, make arrangements with some of your students to create more some time in the next day or two. You'll also need to cut and color the pattern strip (Blackline NC 25) to match the sequence the class has selected. Finally, decide whether you want to glue numbers to the markers ahead of time this month or have children help you do so as they're posted on the grid each day.

. . . .

A Link Each School Day How Many Days Have We Been in School This Month?

Skills

★ counting by 1's

★ counting by 10's to 100 and beyond

★ adding "1 more"

You'll need

★ 1″ × 7″ paper strips

★ glue

After they've had a chance to explore some different patterns and select one for the calendar markers, take time for a little wiggle, and then direct students' attention to the A Link Each School Day display. How many school days have passed in April so far? Select a helper to construct a new paper link for today.

A Link Each
School Day

Day 2 Introducing the April Daily Routines (cont.)

Our Month in School Setting the Stage for a New Probability Experiment

Skills

★ exploring probability

★ recording data

You'll need

★ Dog & Cat cards (Blackline NC 26, run copies on cardstock and cut the cards apart along the heavy lines. You'll need at least I for each student to color, and 30 or more cards in total.)

★ Cat & Dog spinner

★ a chalkboard, chalk, and eraser, *or* white board, marker, and eraser for each student

★ yellow and brown crayons to share

Once today's link has been posted, explain to the children that you're going to use a new spinner this month to decide what kind of card to put in the Our Month in School chart each day. Show them your Cat & Dog spinner and ask them to share any observations they may have. Children are almost sure to comment on the fact that the cat has more room on the spinner than the dog. Which animal, if either, do they think might come up most if you were to make ten spins? Encourage children to share their reasoning as they make predictions. Does the difference in the spinner have any effect on their predictions?

> ***Teacher*** *This month, we have a new spinner to help us decide what kind of card to put up on the Our Month in School chart each day. What do you notice about this spinner?*

> ***Children*** *Cute! A dog and a cat.*
> *We get to put up dog and cat cards.*
> *How come the cat gets more room?*
>
> ***Teacher*** *What do you mean?*

Day 2 Introducing the April Daily Routines (cont.)

Ella *Look at the spinner. The dog only has a little bit of room and the cat gets almost the whole thing. I don't think this spinner is very fair.*

Children *Yeah! The dog hardly gets any of the spinner.*
The cat gets a really big spot.
I like that, 'cause cats are my best!
I get scared when I see a dog. They bark.
Cats can scratch you. See my scratch?

Teacher *You folks are making some very interesting observations about this spinner. Some of you commented that the cat has more space, and Ella said she doesn't think this is a fair spinner. What do you think will happen if we spin the arrow 10 times on this spinner? Do you think the arrow will land on one or the other of the 2 animals more often?*

Children *I want the dog to win. He looks like my dog.*
Dogs are way bigger than cats—the dog will win, for sure.
Dogs are stronger, too.
Cats can run faster. The cat will win this race.

Teacher *Do you think it matters that the dog doesn't have as much room on the spinner?*

Ella *Yes! It's not fair. The arrow's going to land on the cat way more.*

Although it's hard to predict what will come from any particular group of children, comments about the nature of the spinner, such as Ella's observation that the cat occupies more space than the dog and for that reason will be spun more often, tend to be the exception rather than the rule in kindergarten. The good news is that you don't have to do anything more than listen, encourage your students to share their reasoning, and then provide the experience that will allow them to test their ideas. What they will discover over a month's time is that the arrow lands on the cat more frequently, despite the fact that the dog is bigger, more powerful and, in the eyes of some, more lovable. This may be a bit of a puzzle to some of your children, but not one that you have to explain in any formal way. The experience of collecting data over a period of 20 days or so, representing the information, and musing over the results is sufficient.

After students have had a chance to make some predictions, have them each collect a set of writing materials (board, marker, and eraser) and rejoin you in the circle. Tell them that you're going to spin the arrow ten times, and that you want each of them to keep score on their board. You may, as you did last month, ask children to invent their own methods of recording the results. You might also consider sharing some kind of simple system with them, such as dividing their board in two, labeling the sides in some way, and making a

Day 2 Introducing the April Daily Routines (cont.)

mark on the appropriate side for each spin.

> *Teacher* *This time, let's all set up our scoreboards the same way. I'd like you to draw a line down the middle of your board. Now label one side with a C for Cat, and the other with a D for Dog. You can draw a little picture of each animal too, if that will help you tell the 2 sides apart. Each time I spin, I'd like you to make a mark on the side of your board that shows whether the arrow landed on the cat or the dog.*

When everyone is ready, spin the arrow ten times while they keep score. Then discuss the results.

> *Children* *The cat won!*
> *The cat got lots—the dog hardly got any.*
> *The cat got 1 2, 3, 4, 5, 6, 7 and the dog only got 3.*
> *Cats can run faster.*
> *I think the cat got more 'cause it's got more room on there. That spinner isn't fair.*

> *Teacher* *What would a fair spinner look like?*

> *Marco* *It would be part for the cat and part for the dog, like last time with the frog and that other one.*

> *Teacher* *The spinner would be divided equally, half for the cat and half for the dog?*

> *Marco* *Yes.*

After a bit of discussion, promise the children that you'll spin the spinner every day to see if the cat or the dog comes up, and keep score by placing a card for that animal in the Our Month in School chart, as well as by marking a graph. By the end of the month, each of the animals will have had plenty of chances to win.

Conclude today's session by having children help prepare the Cat & Dog cards. You'll need 15 cats colored yellow and 15 dogs colored brown. (If you have more than 30 children, save the extra cards for other purposes.)

Day 3

CALENDAR COMPONENTS

Introducing the April Daily Routines

Today, children bring the calendar grid up to date, posting the April markers according to the pattern they developed yesterday. Then they attach a new link to the paper chain and spin the Cat & Dog spinner three times, collecting cards for the first three days of school graphing the results, and exploring some other ways to represent the information. Finally, introduce a new game with the bean clock.

. . . .

The Calendar Grid Getting Started

Skills

★ reading and extending a pattern

You'll need

★ calendar markers

★ April pattern strip, colored in to match the pattern your class developed yesterday

★ Calendar Numbers, unless you've already glued them to your calendar markers

Open today's session by inviting children to join you in front of the Number Corner display. Show them the pattern strip for the month, which you've prepared to match the pattern they chose yesterday. (We've colored in the strip above to be an AABBB pattern—cat, cat, dog, dog, dog—but your class may have chosen something different.)

Which animal, the cat or the dog, will have to be posted first on the calendar grid, and where? It's the third school day of the month, but it might be the 4th or 5th of April, depending on the day of the week the month began. With children's help, figure out how many markers need to be displayed to bring the calendar grid up to date. If you haven't already glued numbers to the markers, the students will also need to help you with this task.

Day 3 Introducing the April Daily Routines (cont.)

· ·

A Link Each School Day & Our Month in School

Skills

★ counting by I's

★ exploring probability

★ using a graph to record data

★ representing data in a variety of ways

You'll need

★ I" × 7" paper strips

★ glue

★ the Dog & Cat cards children colored yesterday (You'll need 15 of each card, cats colored yellow and dogs colored brown)

★ Cat & Dog spinner

★ Cat & Dog graph (Blackline NC 27, run a single copy and post it alongside the Our Month in School chart)

★ a yellow crayon and a brown crayon

★ helper jar

★ a chalkboard, chalk and eraser, or white board, marker, and eraser for each student

Once the calendar grid has been brought up to date, direct children's attention to the task of recording the number of days they've been in school this month. Select a helper to attach a new link to the paper chain for April. As he's working, explain that you're going to have some helpers spin the Cat & Dog spinner to see which cards should be posted for the first three days of school this month. Based on yesterday's experience, what do the children think will happen?

> **Teacher** *Here's our Cat & Dog spinner. We're going to spin the arrow 3 times today, because we've been in school 3 days so far this month. We need to start getting our Cat & Dog cards placed on the chart. What do you think will happen if we make 3 spins today?*

> **Children** *I think we'll get the dog 3 times because he's the best. Cats are cuter. I think they'll win today.*
> *Cats won way more yesterday, though—remember? I bet we'll get more cats.*
> *I think the cat's going to get more. The dog doesn't get many spins.*

> **Teacher** *Why do you think that is, Sarah?*

> **Sarah** *I just know it. My brain told me.*

> **Dianna** *I think it's 'cause the dog only has a little place on the spinner.*

Day 3 Introducing the April Daily Routines (cont.)

After a bit of speculation, choose three different helpers in succession to spin the arrow and post the appropriate cards in the top row of the chart. Discuss the results with students and color in the graph to show what happened. Then quickly distribute boards, markers, and erasers, and ask children to think of some way they can show the results on their boards. How many cats and how many dogs are on the chart?

> *Teacher* *Now that we've spun the arrow 3 times—once for each school day we've had in April so far—I'd like you to think of some way to show these results on your boards. What can you draw or write that will show how many dogs and cats we have on our chart so far?*

Our Month in School

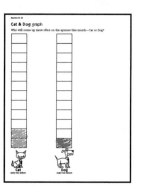

> *Children* *It goes cat, dog, cat. It's a pattern!*
> *It's 2 cats and 1 dog—3!*
> *It goes 1, 2, 3.*

> *Teacher* *Those things are all true. Let's see if you can show what you know on your boards. You can use numbers, pictures, or words.*

Although it would be possible to lead students through writing an addition sentence such as 2 + 1 = 3 to represent the data that's been collected so far, what you're asking them to do here is a bit more open-ended and, in some ways, more powerful. By requesting that children come up with their own methods of representing the information, you are providing an opportunity for them to build new understandings around number and data concepts.

If you are using the full *Bridges* program, your children will be familiar with the idea of communicating what they see and know, both orally and in graphic form (pictures, numbers, words). If you're using a different math program,

Day 3 Introducing the April Daily Routines (cont.)

however, this may be relatively new territory and a few of your students may not be sure of what to do. We encourage you, in this case, to restate the problem and give it a bit of wait time before jumping in to help. Chances are, some of the children will find a way to respond. When they do, ask these youngsters to share their work with the rest of the group. Then give everyone another minute or two to either add something to what they've already recorded or to make a first try at showing something on their boards. Typically, children's responses to this sort of task run all the way from drawing a picture of the situation to writing some form of number sentence, with many variations in between, some of which are shown in the illustration below. Each one of these responses is a valid representation of the data and carries meaning to the child who created it. If you don't see a range of representations today, don't worry, and don't belabor it. You'll return to this task several times or more this month, and with repeated requests and encouragement from you, students will gain confidence and depth in representing data with pictures, numbers, and possibly even words.

"A major responsibility of teachers is to create a learning environment in which students' use of multiple representations is encouraged, supported, and accepted by their peers and adults. Teachers should guide students to develop and use multiple representations effectively. Students will thus develop their own perceptions, create their own evidence, structure their own analytical processes, and become confident and competent in their use of mathematics."

—Principles and Standards for School Mathematics, National Council of Teachers of Mathematics, 2000

Day 3 Introducing the April Daily Routines (cont.)

. . . .

The Bean Clock Match the Clock

Skills

★ reading time to the hour

★ matching visual information

You'll need

★ the Bean Clock

★ Hour Clocks (First 5 cards in the set today—the ones that show 1:00, 2:00, 3:00, 4:00, and 5:00)

★ pocket chart

★ helper jar

After working with the Our Month in School chart, have students put their writing materials away and rejoin you for one more quick game. Match the Clock assumes that you spent some time last month familiarizing your students with the clock face. If you didn't, we recommend that you go back and review The Bean Clock: Introducing the Idea of Telling Time, on pages 234–235, and also Beginning to Tell Time to the Hour on page 240 over the next week or two, and then come back to this game. If you already did those lessons, and your children are starting to become familiar with telling time to the hour this game should be just right.

Display the clock cards in your pocket chart in random order. Then set the hands on your cardboard clock to match one of these cards. Read the time shown with the children and invite them to search for the matching card. Use your helper jar to choose a student to remove that card from the pocket and hold it for now.

Repeat this until all five cards have been removed from the pocket. Then set your clock back at 1:00, and moving it ahead an hour each time, read the times from 1:00 to 5:00 as the five helpers return their cards to the chart in order.

Day 4

CALENDAR COMPONENTS

Continuing Through April

By now, you've introduced all the daily routines for April, including the new pattern on the calendar grid, the paper chain, the Cat & Dog spinner and cards for the Our Month in School chart, and the bean clock. Here are some ideas to consider as you use these routines to create short Number Corner sessions throughout the rest of the month.

· ·

The Calendar Grid

• Take a session or two to post the April birthdate markers on the calendar grid with your students.

Teacher *Let's look at the April markers to see who has a birthday coming up.*

Ligia *I already had mine, but my party's on Saturday.*

Teacher *Where should we put Ligia's marker? Where does it belong on the grid?*

Children *That's easy—it goes on the number 2. She gets to have hers in a pocket with a cat. She's lucky!*

Teacher *You're right about that. Whose name is on the next card?*

Julie *That's my card. My birthday is on Tuesday. That's what my mom told me today.*

Teacher *It sounds like you've been keeping track on the calendar at home. Let's look at our grid here. Where should we put Julie's marker? Is it going to land on a Tuesday on our calendar too?*

Day 4 Continuing Through April (cont.)

Children *Let's count.*
Her number is 17.
I can just go from 9—10, 11, 12, 13, 14, 15, 16, 17.
1, 2, 3, 4, 5, 6, 7, 8, 9, 10, 11, 12, 13, 14, 15, 16, 17.
I see where it goes—I'll show you!

Teacher *Can anyone tell me where to put Julie's marker?*

Children *Kind of under that dog.*
In the number 3 row.
It goes after the 9—you have to keep counting.

Teacher *Good job! Julie, why don't you come up here and put your card where it belongs? Boys and girls, let's use Katie's idea and count on from the 9 to find the right pocket for 17.*

Teacher *Is Julie's birthday on a Tuesday?*

Children *Yep! Sunday, Monday, Tuesday!*
It's under that T day, the one like Tommy.

• Once the April birthdate markers have been posted, you can use them to explore the passage of time and to help children become more familiar with the structure of the grid itself. Here are some types of questions you might ask about the markers:

Whose birthdate is first this month? second? third?
How many days will it be until the next birthdate?
On what day of the week will it be?
Whose birthdate is coming up in eight days?
Who has a birthdate on a Monday this month?

• Continue to have children predict what the new calendar marker will be each day, using the pattern strip to help as necessary. On the days you don't have time to get to the Number Corner, have a helper post the calendar marker and the paper chain link.

Day 4 Continuing Through April (cont.)

• If you elected not to put the calendar numbers on ahead of time, you might display the rest of them, in random order on a nearby bulletin board, or even in the bottom few pockets of your calendar grid pocket chart. As the calendar marker goes up each day, have a helper locate the number that needs to be attached.

• Continue to model how to read the day and date every so often:
Today is _____, April _____, _____.
Be sure to point to the day name, the month, the marker number, and the year label as you chant the date.

• Have children practice writing the numerals for the day's date in the air, on the rug, on individual white boards or chalkboards, or on the appropriate Numeral Writing Practice Pages (Blacklines NC 6–NC 15).

A Link Each School Day How Many Days Have We Been in School This Month?

• Continue asking a helper to add a link to the chain each day. When ten links are in place, change colors and start the second group of ten.

• Once or twice this month, you might have the children determine the total number of days they've been in kindergarten, counting the links on the two sections of the yearlong chain by 10's and 1's, and then "counting on" with the links you've posted for April so far.

Our Month in School Exploring Probability With the Cat & Dog Spinner

• Continue spinning the Cat & Dog spinner each day, and adding the designated card to the Our Month in School chart. Be sure to record the results of the daily spin on the Cat & Dog graph so children can see the information represented in two different ways. Take a few minutes every so often to discuss the cumulative results of this probability experiment. Is the arrow landing more often on the cat or the dog? Is either animal way ahead, or are they about even? If there is a sizable difference, why might that be? How many times has the arrow landed on the cat? On the dog? How many more are there of one animal than the other so far?

Day 4 Continuing Through April (cont.)

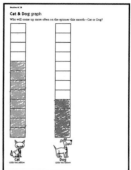

Teacher *What do you notice about the cats and dogs on our chart so far?*

Children *Cats are way more.*
We got a cat today.
There's a dog and then a cat in that row.
1, 2, 3, 4 dogs.

Teacher *How many cats are there on the chart so far?*

Children *1, 2, 3, 4, 5, 6, 7, 8—8 cats.*
There's 4 in the top row. Then another—that's 5. Then 6, 7, 8.

Teacher *Why do you suppose there are so many more cats than dogs so far?*

Children *'Cause cats are faster!*
I bet the dogs are going to catch up.
I think it's the spinner—it's just how it works.
The arrow keeps landing on the cat.

Teacher *Why?*

Children *That's just how it is.*
The cat has a lot more room on the spinner than the dog.
I still think the dog's going to win 'cause he's bigger.
He doesn't have a bigger place on that spinner.

• Take time once or twice a week to have children represent the data collected so far on individual chalk or white boards. Encourage them to use pictures and numbers both, and compliment all the different ways they're able to show the information. You'll probably want to limit children's work to one

Day 4 Continuing Through April (cont.)

row at a time, asking them represent the data that's been collected in the second row during one session, and the third row during another session. It may help to mask the rest of the chart with a piece of paper for this purpose.

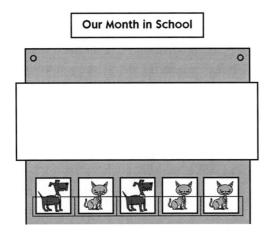

Teacher *Let's look at the cards we've collected in the third row this week. I'll cover over the first 2 rows with a piece of paper so you don't get confused. Can you show on your chalkboards how many dogs and how many cats there are in the third row?*

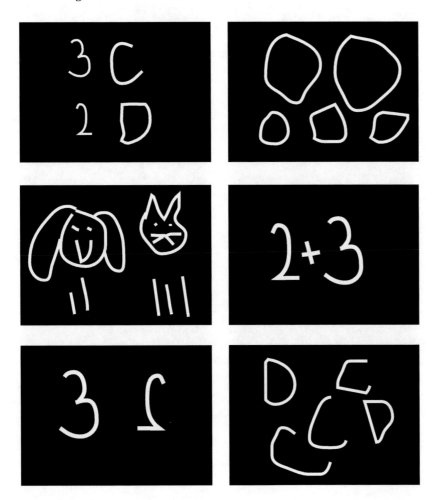

Day 4 Continuing Through April (cont.)

• If you want to write addition sentences to reflect the number of cats and dogs on the chart from time to time, you'll find a record sheet like the one shown below in the blacklines (Blackline NC 28).

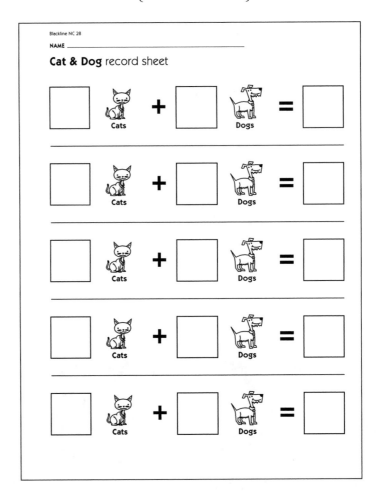

. . . .

The Bean Clock Match the Clock & the Clock Poem

• Repeat Match the Clock, as described in this chapter on page 264, for the other five clock cards in the set.

• On another day, hand out all ten clock cards at random. Set the bean clock to 1:00 and ask children to figure out who's holding the clock card that shows the matching time. Have that child post the card in the pocket chart. Continue moving the hands on your clock forward an hour at a time as children work together to read the time and help each other bring the cards to the pocket chart.

• Find the Clock Poem in the Poems & Songs Portfolio A and put it together in the form of a wall chart or a big book.

Day 4 Continuing Through April (cont.)

The Clock

I, 2, Ready, go!
One o'clock,

Read it to the children several times to establish the rhythm, and then hand out the ten clock cards at random. Have the ten children who are holding cards sit, in order, on a line of ten chairs you've prearranged. As you and the rest of the children begin the poem, have each of the ten stand when his or her time is called out. Be sure all ten students hold their clock cards up in front of them for the audience to see. When you reach the last word in the poem—"snore"—have all ten sit down in their chairs and pretend, very quietly, to go to sleep. Then ask these students to hand their cards to classmates and begin the activity all over again. This is such a catchy little rhyme that it won't be too long before everyone is chiming in on the "more" and the "snore." If you come back to this activity several times, many of your children will know the poem by heart by the end of the month.

Notes

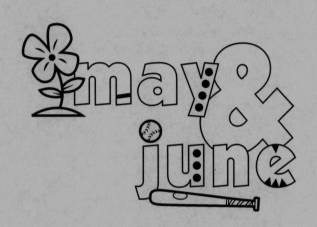

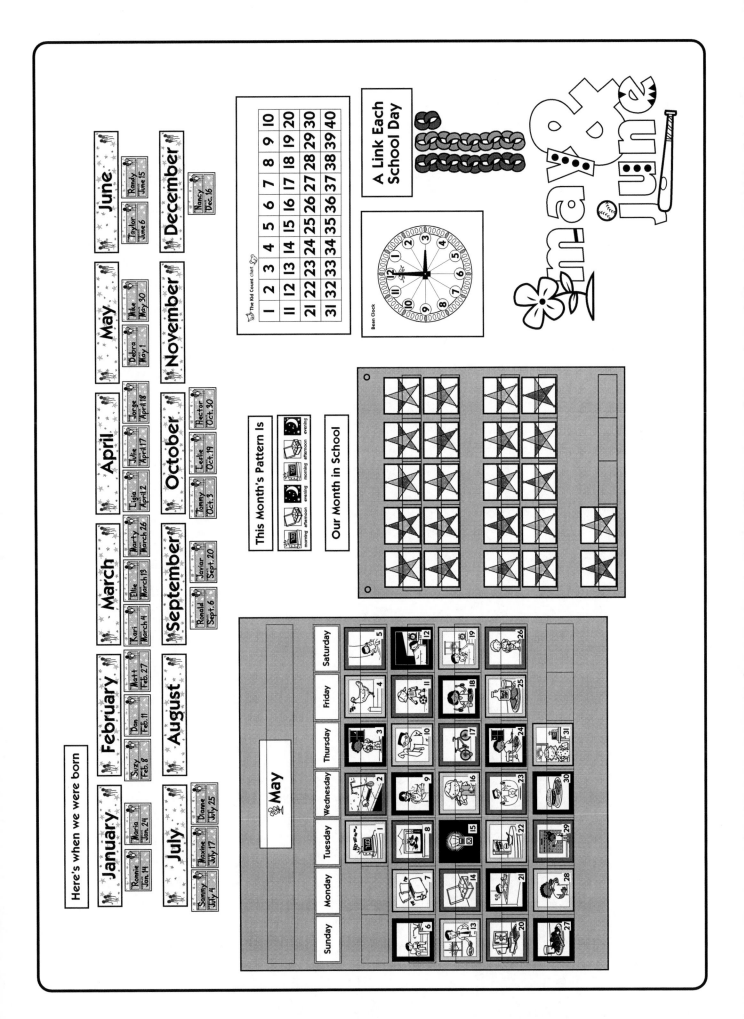

Here's when we were born

January
Ronnie — Jan. 14
Maria — Jan. 24

February
Suzy — Feb. 8
Dan — Feb. 11
Matt — Feb. 27

March
Kari — March 4
Ellie — March 13
Marty — March 26

April
Ligia — April 2
Julie — April 17
Jorge — April 18

May
Debra — May 1
Mike — May 30

June
Taylor — June 6
Randy — June 15

July
Sonny — July 4
Maxine — July 17
Dionne — July 25

August

September
Ronald — Sept. 6
Javier — Sept. 20

October
Tommy — Oct. 3
Leslie — Oct. 19
Hector — Oct. 30

November

December
Nancy — Dec. 16

The Kid Count chart

1	2	3	4	5	6	7	8	9	10
11	12	13	14	15	16	17	18	19	20
21	22	23	24	25	26	27	28	29	30
31	32	33	34	35	36	37	38	39	40

Bean Clock

A Link Each School Day

may & june

This Month's Pattern Is

morning afternoon evening evening morning afternoon

Our Month in School

May

Sunday	Monday	Tuesday	Wednesday	Thursday	Friday	Saturday
		1	2	3	4	5
6	7	8	9	10	11	12
13	14	15	16	17	18	19
20	21	22	23	24	25	26
27	28	29	30	31		

. . . .

Introduction

It's May and another school year is almost over. You'll find plenty of fresh chal-
lenges and intriguing problems this month, and some suggestions to carry you
into June if your school year extends that far. As the year draws to a close, we
encourage you to hold steady with Number Corner instruction through Field
Day, school trips, assemblies, kindergarten graduation, and other special year-
end events. You'll find that it will provide a continued sense of routine, so important to five and six year olds, and also bring closure to a set of activities that
have been significant in children's lives over the past eight months.

Shifting the Number Corner display from April into May and learning the new
routines will take all of your math time for the first three days this month. Once
the daily routines have been established, you should be able to ease back into
shorter Number Corner sessions and return to your regular math instruction.

The Calendar Grid

This month's calendar pattern revolves around events that usually happen in the morning, during the afternoon, or in the evening. You'll introduce this theme by sharing a poem and a set of time-related pictures with your students. After these pictures have been sorted by time (morning, afternoon, or evening) and colored in by the children, they'll be used as calendar markers and patterned according to the time of day they usually occur.

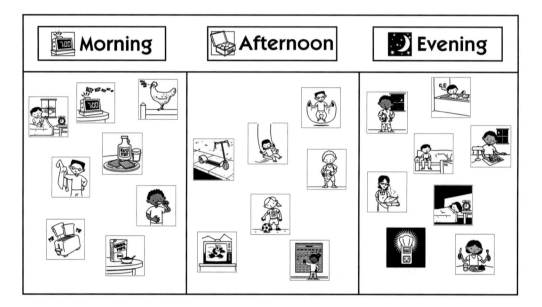

The challenge is that the pictures themselves never repeat—there are 31 different events and objects in the set, sorted and then patterned by time rather than appearance. While some children will respond quite eagerly to the complexities of this problem, others will find it difficult to discern any pattern at all. We suggest that you back the pictures in three different colors of construction paper (yellow for morning, blue for afternoon, and black for evening) before you start to post them on the calendar grid, in order to help all of your students maintain a sense that the markers are patterned, and not just being placed on the grid at random throughout the month.

morning   afternoon   evening   morning   afternoon   evening

The Yearlong Paper Chain

As May opens, children will count the links they collected in April and add them to the second section of the yearlong chain to determine how many days they've spent in kindergarten so far this year. You'll find some suggestions at the end of this chapter for bringing closure to this yearlong effort.

Our Month in School Counting by 5's with 5-Pointed Stars

In keeping with the calendar pattern, one-third of which is devoted to events that usually occur at night, the cards for the Our Month in School chart this month are 5-pointed stars, which the children will color. (You can also have them glitter the 5 points to make them stand out.) You'll add one star a day to the chart and use the cards to help children learn to count by 5's.

The Here's When We Were Born Graph

The Here's When We Were Born graph is another, more compact, version of the Here's When We Were Born chart, which will allow you to honor everyone's birthdates, especially those children born in the summer, and also provide some practice over the month at reading and interpreting information on a graph. To make this display, you'll draw up a graphing form on a large sheet of butcher paper, and have children color and write in the information on a second set of markers.

You'll collect the colored and labeled markers, sort them by month, and put the sorted sets in order from January through December. Then, as the days pass in the Number Corner, you'll glue the markers to the graph a row at a time, asking children to respond to such questions as, "Which month has the most birthdates so far?" and "How many markers are there on our graph so far? How did you count them?" and "Are there more birthdates in February or March? How many more?"

After all the birthdate markers have been posted on the graph, you'll high-light the summer birthdates as a way of recognizing the children who won't be at school when their special days arrive.

Here's	when we	were born.			
❄January	Ronnie Jan. 14	Maria Jan. 24			
February	Suzy Feb. 8	Dan Feb. 11	Matt Feb. 27		
March	Kari March 4	Ellie March 13	Marty March 26		
April	Ligia April 2	Julie April 17	Jorge April 18		
May	Debra May 1	Mike May 30			
June	Taylor June 6	Randy June 15			
July	Sammy July 4	Maxine July 17	Dianne July 25		
August				Our Special Summer Birthdates!	
September	Ronald Sept. 6	Javiar Sept. 20			
October	Tommy Oct. 3	Leslie Oct. 19	Hector Oct. 30		
November					
December	Nancy Dec. 16				

Day 1

CALENDAR COMPONENTS

Introducing the Daily Routines

To open the month of May, students count the paper links they collected in April and add them to the yearlong chain. Next, share a new poem about time and with the children's help, create a set of calendar markers that revolve around the theme of morning, noon, and night. (Because the process of making the calendar markers is fairly involved this month, we suggest that you remove the April markers from the calendar grid yourself, either before today's lesson, or while the children are coloring in the new markers.)

. . . .

The Yearlong Paper Chain & A Link Each School Day

Skills

★ counting by 1's

★ counting by 10's to 100

★ reading numbers above 10

★ counting on from 100

★ adding "1 more"

You'll need

★ yearlong paper chain

★ the links you collected in April

★ 1" × 7" construction paper strips (continue to use the same 2 colors)

★ scissors and glue

★ Paper Chain number labels for 140 through 160, with large paper clips attached

Open today's session by gathering children to the Number Corner. When they've all arrived and settled, direct their attention to the paper chain links they collected in April.

Day I Introducing the May/June Daily Routines (cont.)

How many tens are displayed? Are there any additional ones? How many links are there in all for the month of April? Count them one by one with the children and remove them from the calendar display. Then work with students to attach these links to the second section of the yearlong chain. (Leave the first section of 100 hanging where it is.) You'll probably have to do a little cutting and gluing, and perhaps some color switching to create all the possible groups of 10 as you attach the new links to the second section of the yearlong chain.

Label any new groups of 10 as necessary, and then count the links in both sections of the yearlong chain by 10's with the children, pointing to the labels as you go. When you reach the 1's, if there are any in the second section of the chain, point to each individual link carefully as you count them. Then ask children to count the links in both sections of the chain a second time, stretching their hands out to show 10 fingers for each group of 10 and clapping as they count the 1's.

Once the class has determined how many days they've been in school so far this year, select a helper to construct the first paper link for May, and attach it to the A Link Each School Day label.

. . . .

The Calendar Grid Making the New Markers

Skills

★ exploring morning, afternoon, and evening

★ telling time to the hour

★ sorting

You'll need

★ Hour Hand, Minute Hand (Poems & Songs Portfolio A, pages PA 44–PA 48)

★ May Calendar Markers (Blacklines NC 40–NC 55, run on white paper or cardstock; see note below.)

★ a sorting chart made of butcher paper folded in thirds and labeled as shown on page 282 (Use Blackline NC 56 to make the headings for the chart.)

★ a yardstick or other pointer

★ crayons for children to share

★ 5" × 5" squares of construction paper in the following numbers and colors: II yellow, I0 blue, and I0 black

. . . .

***Note** If you teach double session, we suggest that you run two sets of the blacklines and have each class deal with the entire set of 31 pictures, even though some students in each group may have to color more than one. Use 1 finished set for the calendar, and save the other for a Work Place sorting activity.*

. . . .

Day I Introducing the May/June Daily Routines (cont.)

Begin this part of the lesson by reading the Hour Hand, Minute Hand poem to your students.

Hour Hand, Minute Hand

Hour hand, minute hand,
Around the clock you go,
Night is over, time to get up,
The sun begins to glow.

Then read the poem a second time and take a few minutes to discuss it with the children. What's going on in each of the pictures? What time does each clock show? Do any of your students get up at 7:00 on school days or earlier? How does the clock look when class starts at your school? Do any of the children eat lunch at 12:00? Do they have an apple, taco, and some milk, or do they eat different things for lunch? What time do they go to bed?

After a bit of discussion, explain that you have some new pictures for this month's calendar markers. These pictures show things that usually happen in the morning, in the afternoon, or in the evening, and you'll need children's help to color them in. Since the pattern for the month is going to be, "morning, afternoon, evening; morning, afternoon, evening," the pictures will need to be sorted according to the time of day they usually occur. Lay your butcher paper sorting chart in the middle of the circle, along with three or four of the pictures. Solicit suggestions from your children about where to set each of the pictures. Under which heading does each belong—morning, afternoon, or evening?

> **Teacher** *Here are some pictures we're going to be using for our calendar markers this month. Since our pattern is going to be morning, afternoon, evening, we're going to need to sort these pictures according to the time of day these events usually occur. Let's take the first one, which shows a plate of waffles and syrup, and a glass of juice. When do people usually eat waffles and drink juice?*

Day 1 Introducing the May/June Daily Routines (cont.)

Children *Morning!*
We have waffles on Sundays sometimes.
We have those kind you put in the toaster.
I like orange juice.
We don't have waffles at our house.
Sometimes we have waffles for dinner.

Teacher *It sounds like those of you who have waffles usually eat them for breakfast. So we should put this card under which heading—morning, afternoon, or evening?*

Children *Morning!*
That's what I said before.
I think it should go by the night place, 'cause we have waffles at night sometimes.

The placement of some of the markers may be debatable. If you teach double session, the children in the morning class may have different ideas than their counterparts in the afternoon. For them, the picture of the girl in her desk will belong under the "morning" heading on the chart, and the picture of the boy riding a bike will belong under the "afternoon" heading. This may be reversed for your afternoon session. We encourage you to follow your students' suggestions within reason, knowing that in order to create an ABC (morning, afternoon, evening) pattern on your calendar grid, you'll need to wind up with 11 pictures under the morning heading, 10 under "afternoon," and 10 under "evening." After students have sorted the first four pictures, set out four more, and then four more, briefly discussing the placement of each and putting things to a vote when necessary.

Teacher *It's very interesting to listen to your ideas about where to put each of our pictures. What about the person in the bathtub?*

Children *Morning!*
No, night time. In my house, we take baths at night.
Me too—bath, then jammies.

Day 1 Introducing the May/June Daily Routines (cont.)

Teacher *Let's put it to a vote. How many of you think the bath picture belongs in the morning? 7? How many of you usually take your baths at night instead? Wow! Looks like we'll have to put the bath picture under the evening heading. What about the boy doing his writing paper?*

Children *Morning!*
That one's easy—we go to school in the morning.

After the children have worked as a group to sort the first 12 pictures, you may want to speed things along by handing the rest to individual students to place as they see fit. Once all of the markers have been sorted onto the chart, count them with the children to make sure there are 11 morning pictures, 10 afternoon, and 10 evening. If there aren't, you'll need to negotiate a few switches. Finally, distribute the pictures to individual students to color in. (You may want to mark each of the pictures with a small M, A, or E as you hand them off to children to remember the categories into which they were sorted.)

. . . .

Note *Once children have colored them, you'll need to glue all of the morning pictures to 5" squares of yellow construction paper, all of the afternoon pictures to squares of blue, and all of the night pictures to black squares. You'll need 11 morning markers, 10 afternoon markers, and 10 evening markers in order to be able to create an ABC pattern for the month. Finally, you'll need to decide if you want to number the markers ahead of time or engage children in numbering them each day.*

. . . .

morning   afternoon   evening   morning   afternoon   evening

Day 2

 CALENDAR COMPONENTS

Introducing the Daily Routines

Today, children bring the calendar grid up to date, using the markers they made yesterday. They also work with you to post the May birthdate markers on the grid and attach a new link to the paper chain. Finally, they help prepare a new set of cards for the Our Month in School chart by coloring in five-pointed stars and marking the points with dots of glitter (if you can endure it) to emphasize the "fiveness" of their creations.

. . . .

The Calendar Grid Getting Started

Skills

★ reading and extending a pattern

★ locating information on a calendar grid

★ determining duration on the calendar

You'll need

★ the calendar markers

★ the May/June pattern strip

★ Calendar Numbers, unless you've already glued them to your calendar markers (Blacklines NC 2–NC 3)

★ the May month heading and markers from your Here's When We Were Born chart (post these directly beside the calendar grid)

Open today's session by inviting children to join you in front of the Number Corner display.

Show them the pattern strip for the month. Let them examine it for a moment and then read it through together.

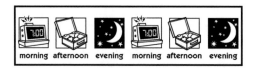

morning · afternoon · evening · morning · afternoon · evening

Teacher *Here's the pattern strip for this month. What do you notice about it?*

Children *There's a moon and some stars.*
I see an alarm clock.
Look at the lunch box.
I think that star one with the moon is at night time.

Day 2 Introducing the May/June Daily Routines (cont.)

Teacher *Great observations! What do you think the pattern is?*

Children *Alarm clock, lunch, stars and moon; alarm clock, lunch, stars and moon.*

Teacher *Those are good guesses. What time of day does an alarm clock go off?*

Children *Morning.*
Oh, I know! It's morning, afternoon, night, like yesterday. Remember when we colored those pictures? Mine was a funny toaster, for morning.

Teacher *Could the word under the alarm clock really say morning?*

Dianna *Sure—it starts with M.*

Teacher *What about the word under the lunch box? What letter does it start with?*

Mike *A, like alligator.*

Ella *I know from yesterday—it's afternoon, and that last one should be night, but it starts with an E.*

Teacher *You folks are doing some fine detective work here. You're right. The pattern goes morning, afternoon, evening; morning, afternoon, evening.*

Once they've had a chance to examine and discuss the pattern strip, ask children to think about the markers they'll need to bring the grid up to date. Because the pictures vary from day to day, you might show students that you've glued the morning markers on yellow paper, the afternoon markers on blue, and the evening markers on black to make it a little easier to tell them apart. It's the second school day of the month, but it may be the 4th or 5th of May, depending on the day of the week the month began. With children's help, figure out how many markers need to be displayed to bring the calendar grid up to date, and whether the pictures should show events that happen during the morning, the afternoon, or the evening. If you haven't already glued numbers to the markers, the students will also need to help you with this task.

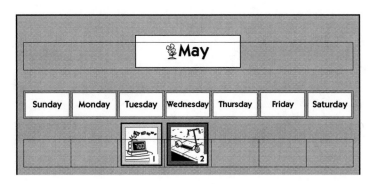

Day 2 Introducing the May/June Daily Routines (cont.)

Once the calendar grid has been updated, draw children's attention to the May birthdate markers. Who has a birthday coming up this month? Ask students to see if they can read the names and numbers on the cards, and then work with them to place one or two of the birthdate markers on the grid in the appropriate pockets right now. If you have more than a couple of birthdates this month, you may want to spread this job out, and not try to place all the markers in one sitting.

> ***Teacher*** *Let's look at the May markers to see who has a birthday coming up.*

> ***Children*** *It's D on the first one.*
> *That's mine! Debra. I had my birthday yesterday.*
> *M for the other one. I know—it's Marty!*
> *No it isn't. It's Mike, for me. My dad says my birthday's not going to come for awhile.*

> ***Teacher*** *What numbers do you see on Mike and Debra's markers?*

> ***Children*** *Debra's is a 1.*
> *Her day already went by.*
> *She gets to have her marker in the pocket with the toaster—boing!*
> *There's a 30 on the other one. That is a long way off.*

> ***Teacher*** *Can anyone figure out which pocket on our grid we'll need to put Mike's marker into?*

> ***Children*** *Count—just count to 30 and then you'll know.*
> *I can do it!*
> *It's going to be clear at the bottom—it's a long time.*

Day 2 Introducing the May/June Daily Routines (cont.)

A Link Each School Day How Many Days Have We Been in School This Month?

Skills

★ counting by 1's

★ counting by 10's

★ adding "1 more"

You'll need

★ 1" × 7" paper strips

★ glue

After they've updated the calendar grid, take time for a wiggle, and then direct students' attention to the A Link Each School Day display. How many school days have passed in May so far? Select a helper to construct a new paper link for today.

Our Month in School Preparing the 5-Pointed Star Cards

Skills

★ observing and describing shapes

★ counting by 1's

★ counting by 5's

You'll need

★ Star cards (Blackline NC 30, run copies on cardstock and cut the cards apart along the heavy lines. You'll need about 24 for the Our Month in School chart, so if you have more children than that or teach double session, plan to use the extras for decorations around the room, or have the students in one group take theirs home.)

★ crayons for children to share

★ glue and glitter or glitter glue (optional)

Once today's link has been posted, explain to the children that you're going to have them help make the new cards for the Days in School chart this month. Show them a copy of one of the star cards and ask them to share any observations they may have. Take a minute to explain that they're each going to color one of the stars, and that they'll be using the star cards this month to practice counting by 5's.

> **Teacher** *Here is one of our new cards for the Days in School chart. What do you notice about it?*

Day 2 Introducing the May/June Daily Routines (cont.)

Children *It's a star!*
My mom showed me how to make one of those.
They're like the stars on the pattern strip—you know, the night place, where it shows the moon and stars?

Teacher *All the cards this month are the same, which is why I'm going to ask each of you to color one. That way, they'll look extra special on our chart. Some people call them 5-pointed stars. Can you see why?*

Joshua *I know! They have 5 points on the ends, see? 1, 2, 3, 4, 5.*

Teacher *You're right. We're going to be using these cards to help us practice counting by 5's this month. Do you see anything else besides the outer points on this star that comes in 5's?*

Ronak *I see 5 triangles.*

Maria *Also, look inside. That shape in the middle has 5 sides.*

Teacher *You have very sharp eyes. You're right—the shape in the middle of this star is called a pentagon, or 5-sided shape.*

Once children have examined and discussed the star, distribute copies and have each child color one of the cards in any color he or she chooses. In order to emphasize the 5 points on the stars, you might also have your students place a dot of glue at the end of each point, sprinkle glitter over the dots, and after a few seconds, shake off the excess to create 5 glittering points of starlight—kindergarten magic!

You'll need about 23 of these star cards for the Our Month in School chart. The rest can be sent home with students or saved to be used as decorations around the classroom.

Day 3

CALENDAR COMPONENTS

Introducing the Daily Routines

Today, children add the next marker to the calendar grid and attach a new link to the paper chain for May. They also post three of the new star cards in the Our Month in School chart and count the star points by 1's and 5's. Finally, they make markers for a display that will highlight the summer birthdates, as well as provide some practice over the month at reading and interpreting graphs.

. . . .

The Calendar Grid What Comes Next?

Skills

★ reading and extending a pattern

★ sorting events by the time of day they occur

You'll need

★ the calendar markers

★ May/June pattern strip

★ Calendar Numbers, unless you've already glued them to your calendar markers

To begin today's session, ask children to join you in the Number Corner. Once they're settled, draw their attention to the calendar grid and have them "read" the markers that have been posted as a helper points to each. Then ask them to make some predictions about today's marker. Although students won't be able to tell exactly what the marker will show, because there are 31 different pictures, they may be able to predict whether it's going to be a morning, afternoon, or evening event. The fact that the pictures have been patterned by when they occur rather than how they look will certainly add another layer of complexity to the problem. Some children may respond quite eagerly to the challenge, while others will find it difficult to discern any pattern at all. You may want to make things a bit easier by naming the markers by time (morning, afternoon, night), or even by background color (yellow, blue, black) so that all of your students maintain a sense that the markers are patterned, and not just being placed on the grid at random.

Day 3 Introducing the May/June Daily Routines (cont.)

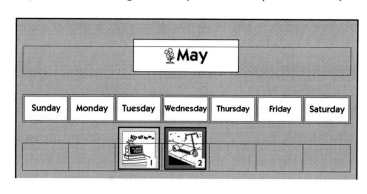

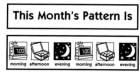

Teacher *Let's look at our calendar grid and see if we can make any predictions about the marker for today.*

Children *We have an alarm clock and then a scooter.*
I bet it's going to be the lunch box.
Maybe it'll be the toast popping up. That's funny.
I like the one with the kid playing soccer—soccer's my best.

Teacher *You're remembering some of the pictures we sorted onto our morning, noon, and night chart. The problem is, there were 31 different pictures. You could probably guess and guess and not identify today's marker. Can anyone think of a way to make our job easier?*

Sammy *It's going to be the hamburger, I bet.*

Teacher *What makes you think that, Sammy?*

Sammy *Well, the toaster is for the morning. The scooter is in the afternoon. The pattern goes morning, daytime, night, so it's time for a night thing. We put hamburgers in the night, remember?*

Teacher *Would it have to be the hamburger to fit the pattern?*

Sarah *It could be the kid sleeping. That's a night thing.*

Teacher *Sammy and Sarah think the picture on today's marker will be something that happens at night because that's what comes next in our pattern. Let's pull the new marker out of the envelope and see what it is.*

Children *It's a kid taking a bath.*
We were right—it is a night thing!
You can take a bath sometimes in the day.

Teacher *So do our markers match the pattern strip so far?*

Children *The pictures don't. There's no alarm clock or lunch box.*
It does match, 'cause on that strip it says morning, afternoon, night.
The colors match too—it goes yellow, blue, black, and I can see those same colors on the back of our markers.

Day 3 Introducing the May/June Daily Routines (cont.)

A Link Each School Day & Our Month in School

Skills

★ counting by 1's

★ counting by 5's

★ adding "1 more"

You'll need

★ 1" × 7" paper strips

★ glue

★ the star cards children colored (and glittered) yesterday

Once the calendar grid is up to date, direct children's attention to the task of recording the number of days they've been in school this month. Select a helper to quickly attach a new link to the paper chain for May. As she's working, have a second helper post star cards in the first three pockets of the Our Month in School chart. (If you had the children decorate their stars with glitter, you may need to paper clip the stars to the pockets.) Then ask children how many points there are on all the stars so far.

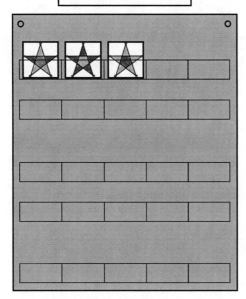

Our Month in School

Children 5!
There's 5 on that one, and 5 on that one, and 5 on that one.
I remember there's 5 'cause I made 5 dots with my glue and put on glitter.
My star is really shiny!

Teacher *There are 5 points on each star in our chart so far—you're right about that. How many points are there altogether? If you add all the points from all the stars on the chart, how many in all?*

Children *We can count them!*
1, 2, 3, 4, 5, 6, 7, 8, 9, 10, 11, 12, 13, 14, 15!
15, I just can count by 5's—5, 10, 15.

Day 3 Introducing the May/June Daily Routines (cont.)

After children have had a minute to consider the problem, have them count by 1's as you touch each star point on the first star. As you do this, have them each hold up one hand, outstretched to represent the star, and touch each of their own fingers, just as you are touching each star point.

1, 2, 3, 4, 5

Continue with the second, and then the third star as they count their own fingers again and then a third time, to 10, and then to 15. Finally, go back and touch each star as you count by 5's. Have children show an outstretched hand for each star as they count with you.

Day 3 Introducing the May/June Daily Routines (cont.)

. . . .

The Here's When We Were Born Graph

Skills

★ naming the months of the year

★ reading and writing numbers to 31

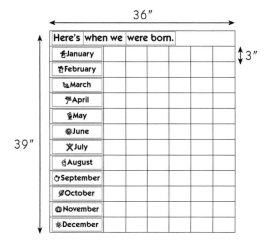

You'll need

★ Here's When We Were Born Markers (Blackline NC 1, run several copies on paper. Cut apart. You'll need 1 marker per child plus a few extras.)

★ a piece of butcher paper 36″ wide and 54″ long, gridded off and labeled to resemble the one shown (Use Blacklines NC 31–NC 36 to create the labels for the graph, or just print right on the butcher paper.)

★ "Months of the Year" (You'll find this song on the cassette tape or CD, *Songs for Number Corner by Greg and Steve*)

★ crayons for children to share

. . . .

Note If you teach double session, you might make two graphing sheets, or make one with enough boxes across to accommodate the data from both classes.

. . . .

Show children the butcher paper you've labeled with the names of the months, and explain that you're going to make a giant graph of all their birthdates. Then take a minute to sing Greg and Steve's Months of the Year song. Do children remember which month their birthdate is in? Do they remember their birthdate? If not, this will be a good chance to review, and also to find out which months have the most birthdates, and which have the fewest. There may even be a month or two in which no one in the class was born!

To end today's session, distribute blank markers to the children and have them color in the balloons, write their name on the line, and fill in their birthdate. If they don't know or remember their birthdate, encourage them to find their marker on the class birthdate chart and copy it.

Day 3 Introducing the May/June Daily Routines (cont.)

After children have finished, collect their markers and sort them by month. Then put the sorted sets of markers in order, from January through December. You'll use these over the next week or two to create the graph row by row during your Number Corner sessions.

Day 4

CALENDAR COMPONENTS

Continuing Through May & June

By now, you've introduced all the daily routines for May, including the new pattern on the calendar grid, the yearlong paper chain, and the Star cards for the Our Month in School chart. You've also had children make markers for the Here's When We Were Born graph, which you'll put together during the Number Corner over the next week or two. Here are some ideas to consider in teaching your Number Corner sessions throughout the rest of the month and into June.

. . . .

The Calendar Grid

• Continue to have children predict what the new calendar marker will be each day, using the pattern strip to help as necessary. On the days you don't have time to get to the Number Corner, have a helper post the calendar marker and the new paper chain link.

• Keep discussion focused on morning, afternoon, and night this month by reading the Hour Hand, Minute Hand poem periodically and discussing the pictures as they appear on the grid from day to day. Which pictures show things that happen in the morning? Which show things that usually occur in the evening? What about the afternoon? Even though each picture is different this month, there's a pattern. What is it and how does it work?

Day 4 Continuing Through May & June (cont.)

> *Teacher* What things do you see on our calendar so far that usually happen in the morning?
>
> *Children* That funny toaster popping up toast.
> Getting dressed!
> Look at that rooster crowing.
> There's a kid brushing his teeth.
> Hey, you know what? All those things have yellow paper behind them.
>
> *Teacher* That's true. I glued all the morning things on yellow to help make it easier to see the pattern. What about the pictures that have been glued on blue paper? When do they all happen during the day?
>
> *Children* After we get home from kindergarten.
> That's when I get to have lunch.
> I like that funny lunch box. I wish I had a lunch box like that.

• If you elected not to put the calendar numbers on ahead of time, you might display the rest of them, in random order, on a nearby bulletin board, or even in the bottom few pockets of your calendar grid pocket chart. As the calendar marker goes up each day, have a helper locate the number that needs to be attached.

• Continue to model how to read the day and date every so often:
Today is _____, May _____, _____.
Be sure to point to the day name, the month, the marker number, and the year label as you chant the date.

• Have children practice writing the numerals for the day's date in the air, on the rug, on individual white boards or chalkboards, or on the appropriate Numeral Writing Practice Pages (Blacklines NC 6–NC 15).

A Link Each School Day How Many Days Have We Been in School This Month?

• Continue asking a helper to add a link to the chain each day. When ten links are in place, change colors and start the second group of ten.

• Once or twice this month, you might have the children determine the total number of days they've been in kindergarten, counting the links on the two sections of the yearlong chain by 10's and 1's, and then "counting on" with the links you've posted for May so far. If your school year ends in May, check the suggestions under the paper chain in June (p. 301) for making a grand display on the last day of school of the links you collected all year long.

Day 4 Continuing Through May & June (cont.)

. . . .

Our Month in School Counting by 5's with 5-Pointed Stars

• Continue to post a new star card in the Our Month in School chart each day. Take time every few days to count the number of stars and total the number of star points on the chart. You might have children count the star points by 1's and then 5's, or just by 5's. We encourage you to do both when you have time, and also to have children continue to point to their own fingers and hands as you point to the stars on the chart. The idea that 5 might be counted as 5 separate objects as well as a single group is somewhat abstract, and the fact that all 5 fingers clearly connect as part of one single hand might help children understand, even if only at a very intuitive level.

1, 2, 3, 4, 5

• Depending on the needs and abilities of your students, you might begin counting the star points over again with each new row, never exceeding 25 at a time. Or, you might start again every two rows, so that the count goes to 50 before you start over. If enthusiasm and interest is high, you might continue to total the points on the stars through the entire month, which will usually bring you to a sum over 100.

• Some days, before you lead children through counting the stars and the star points, pose the problem to them and encourage students to share their counting methods with one another. How are they finding the totals when left to their own devices? Many will need to count one by one to reach the totals. A few may be able to count the points by 5's independently. Some may use a combination of counting methods, as illustrated in the discussion below.

Day 4 Continuing Through May & June (cont.)

Teacher How many stars are posted on our chart today?

Children 7!
5, 6, 7.
I can just see it's 7 because it's 3 more until 10.
1, 2, 3, 4, 5, 6, 7—7 stars.
I know it's 7 because we have 7 links on the chain.

Teacher Great job! How many points are on all of these stars put together?

Children Lots!
That's a lot of counting.
I can do it—I can count my fingers, I think.
It's 5, 10, 15, 20, 25, 30, 35—35 points if you go by 5's.
I know it's 5 and 5 is 10. Then another 10. Then another 10. I think it's 35 or 40.

. . . .

The Here's When We Were Born Graph

• Take a few minutes every day or two to glue a month's worth of birthdate markers onto your butcher paper graph as the children watch and comment. Once you're into February and beyond, you can engage youngsters in counting and comparing the numbers of birthdates in various months. (If you sing the Months of the Year song before your discussion, pointing to the names of the months as they're sung, you may find that your graph talks go a little more smoothly.)

Teacher Now that we've added the April birthdays to our graph, let's take a good look at the data so far. How many birthdays do we have in April, anyway?

Children 2.
Mine and Julie's.

Teacher Which month has the most birthdays so far?

Children That one with the F.
4 is the most.
February—that's when my birthday is!

Teacher Which month has the fewest birthdays so far?

Children That one from today. It only has 2.
My month—it's April. It's only me and Ligia.

Some of the questions you might want to ask about the graph as you continue to post data over the next week or two include:

Day 4 Continuing Through May & June (cont.)

Which month has the most birthdates?

Which month has the fewest?

How many more birthdates are there in _____ than _____?

How many fewer birthdates are there in _____ than _____?

Are there any months in which there are no birthdates at all?

Are there any months that have the same number of birthdates?

How many markers are there on the graph so far? How do you know?

How many markers will there be on the graph when every student's marker is there?

• After all the markers have been posted on the graph, you might want to highlight the summer birthdates by looping them with yarn, coloring those three month-name boxes in yellow, adding special stickers, attaching a sign to the display, or finding some other way to draw them to children's attention. More than likely, you'll be out of school when these students celebrate their birthdates, and highlighting their markers on the graph might be one way to honor them.

Here's when we were born.

❆January	Ronnie Jan. 14	Maria Jan. 24			
⛄February	Suzy Feb. 8	Dan Feb. 11	Matt Feb. 27		
🪁March	Kari March 4	Ellie March 13	Marty March 26		
☂April	Ligia April 2	Julie April 17	Jorge April 18		
🌸May	Debra May 1	Mike May 30			
☀June	Taylor June 6	Randy June 15			
⚔July	Sammy July 4	Maxine July 17	Dianne July 25		
🍦August			Our Special Summer Birthdates!		
🍎September	Ronald Sept. 6	Javiar Sept. 20			
🍂October	Tommy Oct. 3	Leslie Oct. 19	Hector Oct. 30		
🎃November					
❄December	Nancy Dec. 16				

Day 4 Continuing Through May & June (cont.)

. . . .

The Bean Clock Matching the Clock Poem

• Although time figures prominently on the calendar grid this month, we haven't included any activities for reading the clock per se. If the game where children held up clock cards to match the times as they were named in the Clock poem shown below was a hit last month, you might want to bring it back in some of your sessions this month. (If you never got to it last month, be sure to try it a few times over the coming weeks. You'll find two different clock activities described in the April chapter.)

The Clock

I, 2, Ready, go!
One o'clock,

. . . .

What About June?

The Calendar Grid

We're mostly leaving you to your own devices in June. If your school year extends well into the month you may want to make a final set of markers for the calendar grid, here are a few ideas:

• If you teach a double session and you had both groups sort and color a set

Day 4 Continuing Through May & June (cont.)

of time related pictures in the beginning of May, you might mount the second set on yellow, blue, and black construction paper and use them in June. It's the same pictures but sequenced differently, and possible geared toward different time frames (school related pictures having been classified as afternoon rather than morning, for instance), the idea might hold considerable interest for the children a second time around.

• Have children make markers that match a special June theme in your classroom.

• Ask students to brainstorm a list of ideas for June markers and then choose 2 or 3 to make a pattern.

• Recycle the shape markers from September. Given the fact that September's pattern was an ABCDABCD sequence that involved 4 different shapes, it might be interesting to try it again at this late date and see how children respond.

The Yearlong Paper Chain and A Link Each School Day
• As you start into June, have students help count all the links that were collected in May and attach them to the second section of the yearlong chain, Add a link to the Number Corner display each school day in June, and make a grand production of counting all the links on the last day of school. You might even "publish" the results of the yearlong count by attaching all the links from the two sections and any links collected in June to form one long chain, and hanging it in the hall, along with a poster announcing the grand total.

Day 4 Continuing Through May & June (cont.)

Our Month in School

• If you want to display cards in this special pocket chart during June, you might want to make up a new idea, return to one that your children really liked, or use one that they would benefit by revisiting. Consider especially the ten-frame dot cards, you used in December, or the odd/even cards you used in February. Another possibility would be the penny and nickel cards you used in February.

Other ideas for June Number Corner Sessions

• Consider doing the Kid Count again this month in one or more of its many variations. Remember the Number Rock? Distributing the Kid Count cards and having children stand up or sit down as their number comes up in this Greg and Steve song might be a good way to review numbers to 20 (and beyond) with your class. (See January for a summary of the Kid Count lessons.)

• Have children continue to practice reading time to the hour with the Clock poem and clock card games described in the April chapter.